Acclaim for
My Life Through the Seasons
A Wisdom Journal and Planner®

Karin's Seasonal Wisdom Journals are utterly profound and helpful in guiding me on a wondrous journey of my own inner nature whilst keeping me centered. I also appreciate that they provide such a great roadmap for me to go deeper with my feelings, thoughts, dreams, and intentions.

Honestly, this is one of the loveliest and most practical journals I've seen—a journal for busy people, deep thinkers and those, who, like me, love an effortless way to create structure to manifest magic in their life."
   —**Janet Bray Attwood,** *transformational leader* and *co-author of* The Passion Test

"This Wisdom Journal and Planner gives you tools to support and wake up to how much your life matters in our world. If you yearn to create a meaningful life, this journal can inspire you to transform and create the possible that has always resided within you!"
   — **Kitty Fallon**, *Ph.D., professional counselor* and *life coach*

"Over the years, I have used a variety of structured planners in my attempts to balance my work and personal priorities. My Life Through the Seasons has helped me integrate both of these important areas of my life in a single journal and planner. It accomplishes this feat by providing the space to reflect on our important values, passions, emotions, thoughts, and sensations—and then goes one step further by urging us to reflect on what these mean for our lives. As a result, it helps us bring intuition and spirituality into the ways we greet our day and the seasons of our life. Whether you have 10 minutes a day or an hour or more a day to devote to planning and journaling, I highly recommend it!"
   — **Elaine Casquarelli**, *Ph.D., LMHC*

"I have a busy life: full-time job, wife and mother of three active kids. My Life Through the Seasons, A Wisdom Journal and Planner's guided questions and word lists allow me to look inward and assess how I am doing, not just what I have to do. I spend fifteen minutes each morning and five in the evening using my journal. I see the benefit of becoming more aware of my own emotions, intentions and reflecting. More mindfulness has led to more peace and productivity."
   — **Lollie Aulet,** *Special Education Teacher*

"It was a delight to discover My Life Through the Seasons, A Wisdom Journal and Planner. Using it personally has helped me examine my own feelings. We use it in our women's circle as a great way to get insight, get a chance to learn more about each other, and to examine our thinking."
   —**Sylvia Fox,** *writer*

My Life Through the Seasons
A Wisdom Journal and Planner

Fall - Health and Well-Being

Created by
Karin Lubin, Ed.D.

My Life Through the Seasons

A Wisdom Journal and Planner®

Created by Karin Lubin, Ed.D.

karinlubin.com

karin@karinlubin.com

Book design by Jill Conley

Acknowledgments

I could not have done this without those of you who believe in me and this project.

Jill Conley, I could not have created this without your quick insight and understanding—and your amazing artistic gift for creating beauty.

Jim Elferdink, your desire to help me and edit is way beyond what any rational person would do. I am forever humbled by your endless support. My heart expands with you in my world. Thank you, thank you, thank you.

Randy Crutcher, I always feel your never-ending support for me to live my passions. You are my rock, always steady and true.

Thank you to all the clients I have worked with who motivated me to create this. Thanks to all of you who helped me test and refine this journal, especially Lisa Skyhorse, Susanna Maida, Ph.D., Don Eaton, Daniel Will-Harris, Joy Hardin, Dr. Kitty Fallon, Dr. Elaine Casquarelli, Judith Elfrink-Weismueller, Carol Grubbe, Sarah Stout, Cheryl Slover-Linett, Catherine Jones, David Worsley and ShaRon Worsley. Your belief and validation in this offering plus your amazing feedback has meant the world to me.

A humble and deep bow to the many that have inspired me along the way, including, Janet Bray Attwood, Oro Lynn Bensen, Eileen Galbraith, Louise Hay, Christin Kane, Danielle LaPorte, Marci Shimoff, Jenn Sincero and Jan Stringer.

A special, deep acknowledgment to the sky, the stars, the earth and all wild things. Nature keeps me grounded and focused on expanding my heart and listening every day.

Dear Deep Soul

We are at a crucial time of learning a new way to be in this world—a way that integrates the feminine and masculine in each of us, a way where the feminine and masculine are held by each other supportively and lovingly. This journal is an invitation to learn from the incredible power, sustainability, and resiliency of nature and the seasons. This journaling process encourages you to listen to your inner wisdom and remember how deeply we are connected to the earth and it has so much to teach us.

This is a unique journal that emphasizes and builds your emotional intelligence. In many of our cultures, we have developed our masculine side—or our left hemisphere of the brain. We have become so action-oriented we have left behind the emotional connection to our soul and our spiritual unfolding. This journal is about developing our right hemisphere—our more creative, emotional and feminine side. It is a process to guide you to embrace and integrate your wholeness—your being self with your doing self—or your left hemisphere with your right hemisphere.

This journal is for busy people who are deep thinkers, ready to embody a practice of connection to body, mind and soul. Like a "sacred vessel" holding the treasure of your unique interests, feelings and experiences, it connects all your inner explorations, reflections and awareness of who you are and who you want to become. You'll find word lists for feelings to suggest possible new ways of expressing yourself, a body sensation list, and an intention word list to help you become clearer about setting a specific tone and focus for each day. You'll gain greater self-love, acceptance, balance and clarity, as you dive deeper into who you are.

This journal brings you into sync with the four seasons of the year. Each season has a specific theme for your reflection and contemplation as you journal on a daily basis.

Every day after you enter the date, just below you will find a nature prompt. By noticing what is happening in the world outside, the seasons and the moon, you begin to feel more connected to the natural cycles and notice how they are reflected within you. Instead of ignoring these natural influences, you can embrace them, enrich your soul and psyche more consciously, strengthening your body and spirit.

You can find and print a calendar with daily moon phases and celestial events at karinlubin.com/calendar

You'll find your own path as you explore the mysteries of nature—the hidden world within and the seasonal shifts of your outer world. As you do, you'll begin to naturally integrate the feminine with the masculine in visible and invisible ways.

Dive in, be present and enjoy the journey!

Build equanimity, resiliency and hope through your journaling. Commit to five to fifteen minutes daily—or as often as possible—that you can devote to this process. Commitment and repetition are the keys to any successful practice. The more frequent and regular you are, the faster you will notice positive results. This will become a life practice!

Build mindfulness, inner strength and awareness, and feel more grounded through your journaling. When you embrace your wholeness and integrate your "being" with your "doing" you grow stronger.

Open to your heart and to what matters to you through this journaling practice. Express your feelings, enhance your personal vocabulary for your truest expression of your delicious self and give yourself permission to be authentic, real and imperfect—yet completely whole.

Embrace how your psyche is shaped and grounded in the foundation of nature and seasonal shifts. Learn what is moving you as you become more mindful of the seasons and your own inner soul work.

Fall: Health and Well-Being

Fall is a time for harvesting and putting things in order as you prepare to go within during the cold, dark days of the coming winter. You have reaped your abundant "crop" of creativity. Your creative projects of the year have bloomed, fruited and made a positive impact.

Now it's time to harvest the final crops and can, dry or otherwise preserve them for the winter. Trees drop their leaves, flowers die back, and everything is returned to the earth to nourish the soil and provide nutrients for next year. Fall officially begins with equinox when day and night are equal. The days continue to get shorter as we approach winter. What do you need to be well prepared and "stocked" for the winter? What actions, exercises or communications can you do to improve your overall sense of well-being?

Health is the theme for the fall, the season to review all the aspects of your overall health. Health is an integrated and complex weaving of your emotions, your physical body, your mental state and your spiritual life. Use the "Five Aspects of Well-Being" to consider all the elements of wellness and health for a full and vibrant wholeness. When we don't put attention on one aspect, things start to feel out of balance. So, it does not mean you put equal attention on each aspect, but if one aspect is totally ignored that is when a feeling of "being off" or "out of balance" will occur.

How are you supporting your expression of feelings? How are you supporting your physical body to feel strong, energetic and alive? How is your mental state? Do you have the tools to help you move from anxiety to contentment when you want to? How is your spiritual practice—whether that means being out in nature, walking the beach, in a temple or ashram or whatever fills you spiritually?

Notice if the feeling of connection to something larger is fulfilled in your life. Do you experience awe, support, and recognition of the grandeur of life—invisible and visible—on a daily basis? What habits or practices have you created for yourself that support your health and well-being? Notice what those are for yourself. This is your well-being and no one else's. You don't have to compare yourself to anyone else.

If you feel "off" in any aspect mentioned above, notice it, and write it down in your journal. As you begin to unravel the cobwebs and get greater clarity, you can make some practical "habit" changes to support yourself. During these next few months, check in, take notes, reflect on the support you need. Discover the practices that nurture you so you can enjoy your abundance of well-being. As you take stock of your health and well-being, remember you are a powerful manifester of excellent overall health.

Fall Reflection:

Take a moment to write down your thoughts about the season and the theme to prepare for your journal exploration.

What does Fall mean to me?

What books, poetry, movies, and songs feel important for me to connect with this season?

Healing with Nature and Journaling

Writing can be used as a tool for healing and growth, to process, to understand and reflect upon past experiences in your life, your current thoughts and your dreams for the future. By keeping a daily journal, you begin to find greater peace with the difficult parts of your life—transitions, illness, traumas—and you can find that writing brings you the ahas, the epiphanies that help you grow. If you obsess over thoughts and go over them again and again, writing these ideas down can be a great release. It is also helpful to visualize and see what you have written as it moves from your mind to the paper.

When you write, healing begins when you allow a shift in your perspective. Flashes of insight occur and you can begin to find solutions and gain greater clarity. You're going to experience a new freedom by releasing what is going on for you inside and begin to embrace parts of yourself more fully. This journal is designed for your own personal deep dive, with some structure and some open space to connect and experience a whole new level of your being.

Journaling in nature, paying attention to the earth, plants, and animals outdoors can be a healing practice. Scientists have discovered measurable improvements in mental health thanks to this "green couch" or nature-as-therapist approach. Nature provides space for us to reflect—not to mention the health benefits from clean air, sunlight, and exercise. Nature can spark creativity, relieve depression, and diminish anxiety. When you notice you are a connected part of the natural world you feel less alone. You can feel more safe and secure and gain a new perspective about relationships, career changes, health concerns, or loss of loved ones. By writing and observing in nature you begin to notice and observe your thoughts, feelings, and behaviors with the gift of distance. You will find it is easier to view your life from a global perspective and gain clarity about your life and your place in the world.

Research shows that writing can actually provide physical benefits and can boost your immune system. Use this journal to learn from your emotions and begin expressing what is happening for you internally. Tap into your "writing healing powers" and experience your healing bond with nature.

Embodied Journaling

As you journal, you will notice these elements in your writing. You will also become more aware of how these parts fit into your life—your mind, heart, and soul.

Using the Cycles of Nature while Journaling

The cycles of the sun and moon are incredibly fascinating. This journal invites you to notice more about these cycles and reflect on the seasonal and monthly shifts they create as you journal. Sun cycles determine the seasons, and so have been tracked carefully by humans for millennia to help with planting and harvesting of crops and to mark ceremonies and festivals.

The moon has been orbiting around the earth for 4.5 billion years, and as it does, we see the portion that is lit by the sun. One orbit takes about 29.5 days—which is why we have a new and full moon each month. Our moon creates a gravitational pull on the oceans, creating high and low tides. The new and full moon's gravitational pull combines with that of the sun to produce the highest tides. During quarter moons, the gravitational pull of the sun and moon are at right angles to the earth, creating the lowest tides.

You can find calendars showing the phases of the moon and other notable astronomical events at **karinlubin/calendar**
Download and print the three calendars for your seasonal journal and tape or glue onto the blank calendar pages to stay tuned in to the cycles of the moon and planets.

The days that mark the four major divisions of the year are called Quarter Days in the ancient Celtic calendar. We know them as the solstices and equinoxes which start each new season. These dates emphasize the rhythm of nature and guided the way people lived their lives according to the seasons.

An *equinox* occurs when the length of day and night is equal. The northern vernal equinox (that is the beginning of Spring in the northern hemisphere) occurs around March 21st, of each year, and the northern autumnal equinox occurs around September 21st, the beginning of Fall. In the southern hemisphere these dates are reversed.

A *solstice* occurs when the duration of the day and the night is either longest or shortest. The northern winter solstice occurs around December 21st of each year the day is shortest and the night is longest or the beginning of winter. In the north, summer solstice occurs around June 21st. In the southern hemisphere these dates are reversed. Cross-quarter days occur midway between the equinoxes and solstices.

The four *cross-quarter days* are Groundhog Day (February 2), May Day (May 1), Lammas (August 1), and Halloween (October 31). Cross-quarter days indicate that half of the season has passed—an opportunity to celebrate!

Take advantage of the power of the cycles as you journal. For example, a new or dark moon can be the time for our psyche to release old wounds, regrets, or shame and a time to do a healing cleanse for your soul and spirit. What might that look like for you? This could be an opportunity to take some time to assimilate what you learned and practiced over the last month.

A full moon is the time for us to more consciously release the past and set new intentions and focus for the coming month. It is a time to plant seeds or new ideas for your bigger visions. It might be a time to start something new or complete something you have wanted to finish.

Solstices are the time for powerful shifts from the old to the new. Set your new vision and take time to reflect see it, feel it, and dream it.

Equinoxes can be the time to release, re-balance and recalibrate your inner self. Do you feel good, in balance, and on track? If not, what large and small changes need to occur to experience greater balance in your life?

Creating a Positive and Focused Mindset

Setting Intentions

Setting intentions and focusing on your passions every day is a way to support your positive mindset. Ask yourself, "What would I like to focus on or create today?" Use the Intention word list or come up with your **own intention** for the day. If you prefer, you can use visual imagery or different words or sentences to help you. Open a book, a collection of poems, a magazine with images, or use wisdom cards.

Wisdom cards are decks of cards specifically created to help explore your subconscious and provide wisdom and insight. A card you pick might reflect a feeling, an intention, an opportunity or a gift that might not have occurred to you. It may name something you can recognize as true for you.

As you build your emotional intelligence and begin to more consciously integrate your right and left hemispheres, you can begin to look with fresh eyes and see what gifts might be brought to the surface by using these cards. Decks usually come with a guidebook to help you interpret each card. If you pick a card for the day, allow it to reveal to you that which might be hidden.

Using your Daily Pages

Fill in the date and highlight an activity or wellness intention focused on the theme of this journal by entering it in the Physical Activity box. It could be walking, hiking, being out in nature, drinking more water, or taking a bubble bath; you determine what it will be. Whatever you write is what is best for YOU.

There is a **nature prompt** every day to help you connect with nature in a new and special way by noticing what is surrounding you in your natural world. Refer to the calendar you downloaded from **karinlubin.com/calendar** and take note of any moon and planet information for the day.

The **daily question** encourages you to reflect on yourself a little differently. Sometimes reviewing or being asked a question can provide you with new insights. We are constantly changing and to be in the present moment, we need to keep coming back to NOW and seeing what has changed, or how we might have grown.

The next three questions help you to connect with your emotions and right hemisphere. When you explore the multi-dimensionality of feelings (there can be many layers of feelings) you can begin to clarify their triggers and possible solutions. This supports clearer and more effective communication with yourself and others. Use the **Emotion/Feeling word lists** and **Body Sensation word list** to help you expand your inner awareness.

Daily Gratitudes allow you to celebrate the abundance around you and raise your energy. When you express your gratitudes through heart-expanding reflection and see the gifts for today you instantly experience greater happiness and joy.

Using your Daily Focus Planner

1. Write down three or more things you want to accomplish today. Release all thoughts rolling around your brain and put them on paper. This supports your left hemisphere while the other page supports your right hemisphere. Balance and wholeness are the key to experiencing greater peace and harmony.

2. Order them by level of importance (1-3). The most important item to address will be number one.

3. Sometimes you will identify preliminary steps while other times the actual item on your list is all that is needed to complete the task.

4. Now use the day to focus on accomplishing these important items!

5. In the evening transfer the items that you did not get to over to your new list for the next day.

Using your Weekly Reflections and Coloring Meditation pages

Every Sunday the Daily Focus Planner is replaced by Weekly Reflections and Inspiration. Step back, look back over the week, and see what is working for you, and where you might need to make adjustments. Be honest with yourself. Use the following blank page and coloring page to help you relax, access your sense of curiosity, and enjoy art to support your creative flow. The Dalai Lama refers to mandalas (which are in the winter journal) as a visual tool to be used by anyone to discover freedom. I have included other natural imagery (in the other seasons) to support you in also discovering and connecting with our natural world and inner freedom.

Using your Monthly Reflections and Renewal page

At the end of each month, the Daily Focus Planner is replaced by Monthly Reflections and Renewal. Return to your Five Aspects of Well-being—how many aspects are showing up more fully in your life now? Make allowances for a "course correction" for the following month. Hopefully, you will begin to see how your passions and actions are moving you into greater alignment with who you are and where you want to be.

Using Different Journaling Techniques

"Writing practice brings us back to the uniqueness of our own minds and an acceptance of it. We all have wild dreams, fantasies, and ordinary thoughts. Let us feel the texture of them and not be afraid of them. Writing is still the wildest thing I know."
> —Natalie Goldberg

These four seasonal journals guide you with questions relating to the seasonal theme in order to accelerate your exploration, gain greater clarity, and uncover your authentic self in the present moment. There are many ways to journal and get into the flow of writing. Sometimes you might feel stuck or unmotivated to do a lot of writing. Writer's block appears as fear or doubt around what you are going to write about. Here are a few techniques to consider when you need a little inspiration to do some journaling.

Mind Mapping
Rather than just writing, create circles or boxes that represent the flow of your ideas. Start with the main concept—the problem, the project or a difficult concept you want to understand better—and then add branches for the subtopics or action steps. Consider using different colors for the various categories. As you map your ideas, the visual representation will help spark new ideas and understandings.

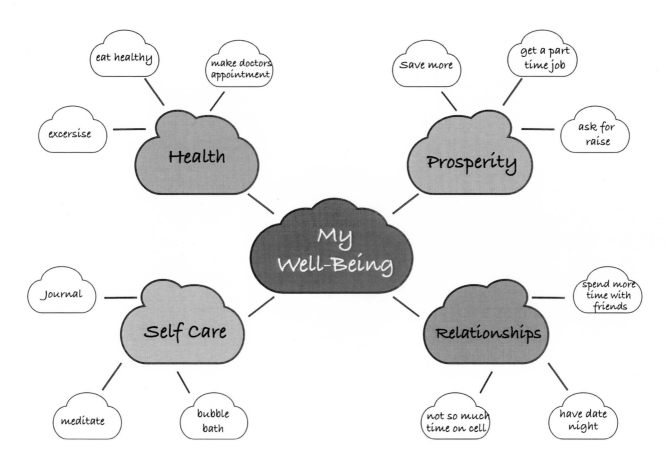

Five- to Ten-Minute Practice

Consider an idea, desire, or heart exploration you want to investigate a little further. Using a blank Notes page in the Journal or a separate sheet of paper, start your timer and begin writing. Allow whatever thoughts that come to you onto the paper without filtering them and without taking your pen off the paper. If you don't know what to write, write, "I don't know what to write" until the next idea comes forward. Don't stop until the timer rings.

What I Mean by That Is… Exercise

When you add this to your writing, you can go more deeply into what is underneath what you originally wrote. Just start each sentence with "What I mean by that is…" The more you write, the more you discover about what is underneath your original thought.

It could look like something like this.

> *I am feeling confused. What I mean by that is I have a niggling bad feeling about this one dream I keep having. What I mean by that is this dream keeps showing me imagery of me sitting in a room all by myself. What I mean by that is I am actually feeling lonely and uncared for right now. What I mean by that is I am ready to find new ways to connect with myself as I know I want to fully show up for ME. What I mean by that is if I can show up for me than I will be able to also show up for others.*

Notes

Using the Five Aspects of Well-Being in Your Monthly Review

The Five Aspects of Well-Being is a visual aid to remind you to always give attention to the five main areas of life. You won't necessarily give them equal attention, but you can create harmony for yourself by assuring all aspects are acknowledged and not ignored.

When you don't put attention on any one aspect (for example, physical or spiritual well-being) you might begin to feel like something is missing. Your health might suffer because you have not taken care of your body or paid attention to symptoms. Or you may feel "empty inside" if you ignore nourishing your soul. In our overly busy western culture, we have become seriously unbalanced, leading to unhappiness, depression, overwork, judgment and lack of purpose in our lives.

The Five Aspects of Well-Being

Physical Well-Being: Health & Fitness, recreation, travel, home, etc.
- What environment makes you feel at peace?
- What fun things do you love to do?

Financial & Career Well-Being: Job, career goals, annual income, dream net worth, financial freedom account, etc.
- What work feels like play?
- What are your gifts and talents?

Relational Well-Being: With yourself, friends, and family.
- What do your ideal relationships look like?
- How do you want to feel with others?

Spiritual Well-Being: Connection to something larger.
- What inspires you — nature, poetry, spiritual growth, creativity, service to others?
- What legacy will you leave behind?

Mental Well-Being: Education, thoughts, emotions, personal development, etc.
- What supports self reflection?
- What do you love studying and can focus on for hours?

Your Seasonal Vision

Use the space below to record what you see for yourself in the next few months. Using the Five Aspects of Well-Being is a great way to begin.

- **Physical Well-Being:** health and fitness, recreation, travel, home, and so on.

- **Relational Well-Being:** with yourself, friends, and family.

- **Financial and Career Well-Being:** job, career goals, annual income, dream net worth, financial freedom account, etc.

- **Mental and Emotional Well-Being:** education, thoughts, emotions, personal development, and so on.

- **Spiritual Well-Being:** connection to something larger.

Remember to notice what season you are in and how that may impact your vision. For example, during the **Winter** months you might want to be sitting with your dreams and allowing them to come to greater clarity while giving them sustenance and warmth. The **Spring** might be more about planting those "seeds" out in the world and seeing how they sprout. In the **Summer** you might be nurturing your vision for others to see and enjoy. And the **Fall** could be harvest time, when what you have created is fully formed and ready to sustain you through the winter months. Now this is just an example. You might find you need to plant your seeds in the fall and harvest in the Spring!

Your Seasonal Vision

Using Your Passion Page

What are you passionate about? What is it that you just can't wait to dive into every day?

I invite you to work with a coach or therapist who is certified as a Passion Test facilitator—or read the books, The Passion Test: The Effortless Path to Discovering Your Life Purpose, by Chris Attwood and Janet Bray Attwood, and The Passion Principle, How to Live Your Most Passionate Life, By Bruce Hutchison and Randy Crutcher. When you know what is really important to you—your passions—you can then make decisions based on them every single day. This decision-making system can become a powerful success habit.

If you have gone through the Passion Test process, then please write down your current five passions. You want to review your passions daily to help you get energized and excited about what is important to you.

Get the support you need to feel greater freedom and give yourself permission to live your life full out. This begins when you daily review your passions and you set your intentions. When you put attention on what matters to you, they begin to show up in your life.

Passion Page
List your five passions

Date: ....

Passion 1:

Passion 2:

Passion 3:

Passion 4:

Passion 5:

Notes

Emotion/Feeling Words

Expanded Feelings

ACCEPTING/OPEN

accepting	confident	fulfilled	receptive	sympathetic
amazed	connected	interested	reliable	understanding
calm	easy	kind	satisfied	
centered	free	peaceful	serene	

ALIVE/HAPPY

animated	ecstatic	frisky	merry	sunny
attractive	elated	glad	optimistic	thankful
awe	enchanted	gleeful	orgasmic	thrilled
blissed	energetic	great	overjoyed	valued
bloom	enthusiastic	joyful	passionate	vibrant
cheerful	euphoric	joyous	playful	wonderful
content	excited	jubilant	provocative	
courageous	festive	liberated	rejuvenated	
delighted	fortunate	lively	renewed	
eager	free	lucky	spirited	

CONNECTED/COMPASSIONATE

accepting	compassion	exploring	intrigued	safe
affectionate	curious	fascinated	involved	stimulated
available	empathy	fulfilled	open	warm
caring	engaged	interested	present	worthy

COURAGEOUS/POWERFUL

adventurous	daring	free	purposeful	sure
brave	determined	gutsy	rebellious	tenacious
capable	dynamic	hardy	secure	unique
certain	engaged	impulsive	spirited	worthy
confident	fearless	proud	strong	valiant

GRATEFUL/HOPEFUL

appreciative	cheerful	expectant	lucky	reassured
at ease	certain	fortunate	moved	relaxed
blessed	comfortable	free and easy	optimistic	serene
bouyant	content	grace	peaceful	surprised
bright	delighted	hopeful	pleased	thankful
calm	encouraged	humbled	promising	touched

INTERESTED/ POSITIVE

absorbed	captivated	delighted	enthusiastic	inspired
affected	challenged	determined	excited	intent
affirmative	concerned	eager	fascinated	intrigued
attentive	confident	earnest	focused	keen
bold	curious	encouraged	hopeful	optimistic
brave	daring	engrossed	inquisitive	trusting

LOVING/TENDER

admiring	close	devoted	passionate	tender
affectionate	comforted	endearing	reflective	touched
attracted	compassionate	fondness	sensitive	vulnerable
calm	connected	loved	self-loving	warm
caring	considerate	loving	serene	warmth

Contracted Feelings

AFRAID/DOUBTFUL

alarmed	disturbed	nervous	restless	terrified
anxious	doubtful	panicked	scared	threatened
apprehensive	fearful	perplexed	shaky	timid
concerned	frightened	quaking	shocked	uneasy
cowardly	grouchy	questioning	skeptical	ungrounded
daunted	hesitant	rejecting	spooked	unsure
dissatisfied	inhibited	reluctant	suspicious	worried

ANGRY/ANNOYED

agitated	edgy	hostile	irate	resentful
aggressive	enraged	impatient	irritated	sore
annoyed	exasperated	incensed	moody	unpleasant
bitter	frustrated	indignant	offensive	upset
boiling	fuming	inflamed	on-edge	unsettled
contempt	furious	infuriated	pissed	vindictive
disturbed	grouchy	insulting	provoked	worked-up

CONFUSED

disillusioned	hesitant	muddled	skeptical	uncertain
distrustful	indecisive	perplexed	stupefied	uneasy
doubtful	lost	pessimistic	tense	unsure
embarrassed	misgiving	shy	unbelieving	upset

DESPAIR

a sense of loss	diminished	forlorn	lonely	terrible
abominable	disappointed	gloomy	longing	unhappy
anguish	discouraged	guilty	lousy	upset
ashamed	disgusted	heartbroken	miserable	weary
despondent	dissatisfied	hopeless	powerless	yearning

EMBARASSED/SHAMED

ashamed	awkward	demeened	mortified	weak
humiliated	chagrined	distressed	self-conscious	worthless
appalled	chastened	inhibited	useless	

HELPLESS/POWERLESS

alone	fatigued	in despair	resigned	victim
defenseless	forced	incapable	tragic	vulnerable
distressed	frustrated	inferior	trapped	woeful
dominated	hesitant	paralyzed	unprotected	
empty	Impotent	powerless	useless	

HURT/ SAD

aching	depressed	heartbroken	offended	upset
afflicted	deprived	hopeless	pained	victimized
agonized	desolate	humiliated	pessimistic	weary
alienated	desperate	injured	rejected	wronged
anguish	disappointed	lonely	sorrowful	yearning
appalled	forlorn	melancholy	teary	
crushed	gloomy	miserable	tortured	
dejected	grieving	mournful	unhappy	

INDIFFERENT

bored	distant	lifeless	ordinary	weary
cold	dull	mediocre	preoccupied	
disinterested	insensitive	neutral	reserved	
detached	lackluster	nonchalant	unremarkable	

STRESSED/TENSE

anxious	depleted	frazzled	rejecting	tight
burned out	edgy	overwhelm	restless	weary
cranky	exhausted	rattled	shaken	worn-out

Intention List

Audacious
Awesome
Alive
Appreciative
Artistic
Authentic
Blissful
Beautiful
Bold
Boundaries
Bountiful
Brave
Bright
Boundless
Build
Calm
Celebrate
Charismatic
Cherished
Clear
Collaborative
Comfort
Commit
Confidence
Conscious
Courage
Cultivate
Creative
Faith
Focused
Dedicated
Determined
Deeply Loved
Delighted
Discipline
Divinely Inspired
Divine

Connection
Divinely Guided
Dream
Ecstatic
Energetic
Excite
Expansive
Expressive
Explore
Faith
Family
Fierce Love
Fitness
Financially Free
Flow
Forgiveness
Free
Freedom
Fresh
Friend
Fulfilled
Fun
Gentle
Generous
Glow
Giving
Goddess
Grace
Grateful
Grounded
Guided
Happy
Healthy
Heal
Holy
Honest
Hopeful

Humble
Ignited
Imagination
In Awe
Integrity
Intentional
Intimacy
Inspiring
Intuitive
Journey
Joyful
Kind
Lead
Learn
Liberated
Light
Lit-Up
Limitless
Listen
Loved
Lovable
Loving
Luminous
Magic
Magnetic
Miracles
Mindful
Momentum
Movement
Mystery
Mystical
Nature
Nurture
Optimistic
Open Hearted
Orgasmic
Organize

Overcome
Peaceful
Passionate
Patience
Peace
Permission
Power
Presence
Present
Prosper
Pure love
Purpose
Question
Quiet
Re-Brand
Radiant
Real
Receive
Relax
Release
Renew
Resolve
Respect
Retreat
Rise
Romance
Safe
Sassy
Satisfaction
Selfless
Seen
Sensual
Serene
Shine
Simplify
Smile
Spacious

Sparkly
Spirited
Strength
Strive
Strong
Success
Surrender
Tender
Thoughtfulness
Touch
Transparent
Transformation
Travel
Trusting
Truth
Tribal
Understand
Unleashed
Unlimited
Unstoppable
Valued
Vibrant
Visionary
Vulnerability
Wellness
Whole
Whimsical
Wild
Win
Wisdom
Wonder
Worthy
Wow
Yes
Youthful

Body Sensation Words

OPEN AND FLUID SENSATIONS

airy	expansive	open	shaky	strong
breathless	floating	pounding	shivery	trembly
bubbly-open	flowing	pulsing	smooth	tremulous
calm	fluid	radiating	soft	vibrating
cool	fluttery	relaxed	spacey	warm
dizzy	light	releasing	spacious	wobbly
energized	loose	sensitive	sparkly	
expanded	luminous	settled	streaming	

CONSTRICTED SENSATIONS

achy	congested	flaccid	numb	sweaty
bloated	constricted	frozen	paralyzed	tender
blocked	contained	full	puffy	tense
brittle	contracted	heavy	queasy	thick
bruised	dark	hollow	rigid	tight
clammy	dense	hot	raw	wooden
clenched	disconnected	icy	sore	
closed	dull	knotted	stiff	
cold	empty	nauseous	suffocated	

ACTIVE SENSATIONS

breathless	fluttery	pulsing	shaky	tremulous
bubbly-open	itchy	queasy	shivery	twitchy
burning	nauseous	quivery	spacey	vibrating
buzzy	nervy	radiating	throbbing	wobbly
dizzy	pounding	ragged	tingling	
electric	prickly	sensitive	trembly	

Thanks to soulalivewomen.com, Larisa Noonan, and The Hoffman Institute.

Notes

You can find a calendar showing the phases of the moon and other notable astronomical events at **karinlubin.com/calendar**

Print the calendar, trim it to fit, and then paste it onto this page.

October

Sunday	Monday	Tuesday	Wednesday	Thursday	Friday	Saturday

Date:_____

What are animals doing when you walk outside?

🍂 *Physical Activity*

Hiked for 3 miles

This Week's Affirmation (say it out loud)
I'm improving my mental and physical health with grace and ease.

What is my Intention for the Day?

Consider using the intention list or a tarot or wisdom card. Your daily card might reflect a feeling, an intention, an opportunity, or a gift that you might not have thought of which gives you greater insight.

I am empowered and claim my birthright.

Question for the Day

What do I feel positive about or grateful for (no matter how big or small I think it is)?

I am deeply grateful for feeling stronger as I move through the years. I love that I eat well, support my body internally and externally and always look forward to showing myself self-care—like taking a hot tub or drinking a healthy smoothie with greens.

Today I am feeling ...

Name or identify my feelings. Refer back to feeling list if needed.

I feel excited. I am maybe a tiny bit nervous. I am happy to be of service to others. I feel hopeful.

What is the sensation of that feeling in my body? See sensation list.

Smile on my face, my heart feels open. I feel nervous—tightness in my shoulders.

What situation or thoughts triggered this feeling?

Teaching a class

What is this feeling telling me about what I need in this situation?

I might consider moving out of my head into my heart even more.
Do some stretching before the class and do some breathing.

I am grateful for:

Waking up with a smile   Exercising today
A welcoming home   Laughing with my partner
Having sweet connections with friends   Completing a project

28

Daily Focus Planner

Write down three or more things or areas to focus on today that are meaningful.
Prioritize and take action!

-Get up early to be able to exercise
-Send to editor
-Connect with friends: Give and receive hugs, make calls

Inspiration, Notes, Drawings & Dreams

What happened today that helped me feel more connected to nature?

I experienced a magical moment outdoors watching the sunset. I loved connecting with a couple of dear friends.

What had meaning for me today? What do I keep ignoring?

Setting a meeting to my boss about my new idea.
Can't seem to complete new webpage easily- need to finish by end of this week!

Date:_____

Study something in nature that you have not examined before.
What do you notice?

This Week's Affirmation (say it out loud)
I'm improving my mental and physical health with grace and ease.

What is my Intention for the Day?

Consider using the intention list or a tarot or wisdom card. Your daily card might reflect a feeling, an intention, an opportunity, or a gift that you might not have thought of which gives you greater insight.

_____

_____

Question for the Day
What do I feel positive about or grateful for (no matter how big or small I think it is)?

_____

_____

_____

Today I am feeling …
Name or identify my feelings. Refer back to <u>feeling list</u> if needed.

_____

_____

_____

What is the sensation of that feeling in my body? See <u>sensation list</u>.

_____

What situation or thoughts triggered this feeling?

_____

_____

What is this feeling telling me about what I need in this situation?

_____

_____

I am grateful for:

_____

_____

_____

Daily Focus Planner

Write down three or more things or areas to focus on today that are meaningful.
Prioritize and take action!

 *Inspiration, Notes, Drawings & Dreams*

What happened today that helped me feel more connected to nature?

What had meaning for me today? What do I keep ignoring?

Date:_____

What insect sounds or activity do you notice today?

This Week's Affirmation (say it out loud)
I'm improving my mental and physical health with grace and ease.

What is my Intention for the Day?

Consider using the intention list or a tarot or wisdom card. Your daily card might reflect a feeling, an intention, an opportunity, or a gift that you might not have thought of which gives you greater insight.

_____

_____

Question for the Day

What have I been holding on to that I am now ready to let go of?

_____

_____

_____

Today I am feeling …

Name or identify my feelings. Refer back to <u>feeling list</u> if needed.

_____

_____

What is the sensation of that feeling in my body? See <u>sensation list</u>.

_____

What situation or thoughts triggered this feeling?

_____

_____

What is this feeling telling me about what I need in this situation?

_____

_____

I am grateful for:

_____   _____

_____   _____

Daily Focus Planner

Write down three or more things or areas to focus on today that are meaningful.
Prioritize and take action!

Inspiration, Notes, Drawings & Dreams

What happened today that helped me feel more connected to nature?

What had meaning for me today? What do I keep ignoring?

Date:_____

Find some earth, grass, or a rock to stand on today. Enjoy.

This Week's Affirmation (say it out loud)
I'm improving my mental and physical health with grace and ease.

What is my Intention for the Day?

Consider using the intention list or a tarot or wisdom card. Your daily card might reflect a feeling, an intention, an opportunity, or a gift that you might not have thought of which gives you greater insight.

Question for the Day

What feeds my body and soul these days? What is one thing I can do today to realize my best self?

Today I am feeling …
Name or identify my feelings. Refer back to <u>feeling list</u> if needed.

What is the sensation of that feeling in my body? See <u>sensation list</u>.

What situation or thoughts triggered this feeling?

What is this feeling telling me about what I need in this situation?

I am grateful for:

34

Daily Focus Planner

Write down three or more things or areas to focus on today that are meaningful.
Prioritize and take action!

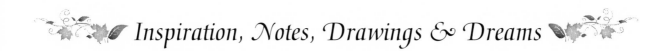

Inspiration, Notes, Drawings & Dreams

What happened today that helped me feel more connected to nature?

What had meaning for me today? What do I keep ignoring?

Date:_____

What colors are still vibrant outdoors?

This Week's Affirmation (say it out loud)
I'm improving my mental and physical health with grace and ease.

What is my Intention for the Day?

Consider using the intention list or a tarot or wisdom card. Your daily card might reflect a feeling, an intention, an opportunity, or a gift that you might not have thought of which gives you greater insight.

_____
_____
_____

Question for the Day

What is my #1 challenge around my relationship to food and how it affects my body image? What can I do to make a tiny shift today?

_____
_____
_____

Today I am feeling …

Name or identify my feelings. Refer back to feeling list if needed.

_____
_____

What is the sensation of that feeling in my body? See sensation list.

_____

What situation or thoughts triggered this feeling?

_____
_____

What is this feeling telling me about what I need in this situation?

_____
_____

I am grateful for:

_____   _____
_____   _____

Daily Focus Planner

Write down three or more things or areas to focus on today that are meaningful.
Prioritize and take action!

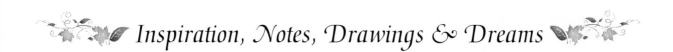 *Inspiration, Notes, Drawings & Dreams*

What happened today that helped me feel more connected to nature?

What had meaning for me today? What do I keep ignoring?

Date:_____

How does the sun feel on your skin today?

This Week's Affirmation (say it out loud)
I'm improving my mental and physical health with grace and ease.

What is my Intention for the Day?

Consider using the intention list or a tarot or wisdom card. Your daily card might reflect a feeling, an intention, an opportunity, or a gift that you might not have thought of which gives you greater insight.

_____

_____

_____

Question for the Day
With whom do I need to create better boundaries in my life? What could that look like?

_____

_____

_____

Today I am feeling …
Name or identify my feelings. Refer back to feeling list if needed.

_____

_____

_____

What is the sensation of that feeling in my body? See sensation list.

_____

What situation or thoughts triggered this feeling?

_____

_____

What is this feeling telling me about what I need in this situation?

_____

_____

_____

I am grateful for:

_____   _____

_____   _____

38

Daily Focus Planner

Write down three or more things or areas to focus on today that are meaningful.
Prioritize and take action!

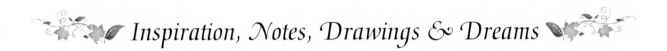

Inspiration, Notes, Drawings & Dreams

What happened today that helped me feel more connected to nature?

What had meaning for me today? What do I keep ignoring?

Date:_____

Look for small insects outside and watch them.

This Week's Affirmation (say it out loud)
I'm improving my mental and physical health with grace and ease.

What is my Intention for the Day?

Consider using the intention list or a tarot or wisdom card. Your daily card might reflect a feeling, an intention, an opportunity, or a gift that you might not have thought of which gives you greater insight.

_____
_____
_____

Question for the Day

What do I notice I could let go of in my life to feel more at peace?

_____
_____
_____

Today I am feeling …

Name or identify my feelings. Refer back to <u>feeling list</u> if needed.

_____
_____
_____

What is the sensation of that feeling in my body? See <u>sensation list</u>.

_____

What situation or thoughts triggered this feeling?

_____
_____

What is this feeling telling me about what I need in this situation?

_____
_____
_____

I am grateful for:

_____   _____
_____   _____

Daily Focus Planner

Write down three or more things or areas to focus on today that are meaningful.
Prioritize and take action!

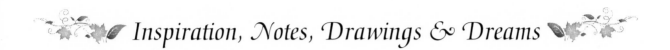 *Inspiration, Notes, Drawings & Dreams*

What happened today that helped me feel more connected to nature?

What had meaning for me today? What do I keep ignoring?

Date:_____

What are animals doing around your neighborhood, park, or land near you?

This Week's Affirmation (say it out loud)
The older I am, the stronger I become in mind and body.

What is my Intention for the Day?

Consider using the intention list or a tarot or wisdom card. Your daily card might reflect a feeling, an intention, an opportunity, or a gift that you might not have thought of which gives you greater insight.

Question for the Day

What does honest, direct communication look and sound like to me? What is an example of communication between myself and someone I'd like to have that with?

Today I am feeling …
Name or identify my feelings. Refer back to <u>feeling list</u> if needed.

What is the sensation of that feeling in my body? See <u>sensation list</u>.

What situation or thoughts triggered this feeling?

What is this feeling telling me about what I need in this situation?

I am grateful for:

Weekly Reflections and Inspiration

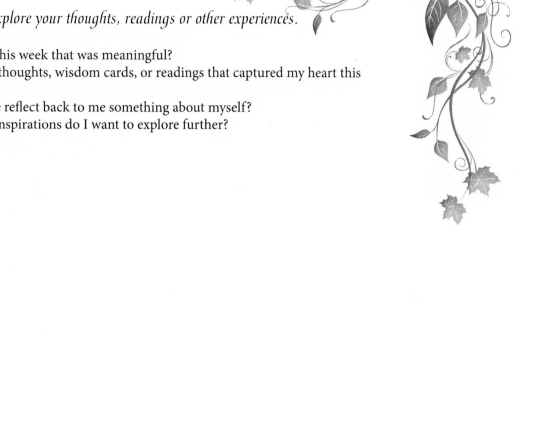

Use this space to explore your thoughts, readings or other experiences.
For example,

- What did I do this week that was meaningful?
- What were the thoughts, wisdom cards, or readings that captured my heart this week?
- How did nature reflect back to me something about myself?
- What ideas or inspirations do I want to explore further?

What are some empowering steps for next week?

Coloring Meditation

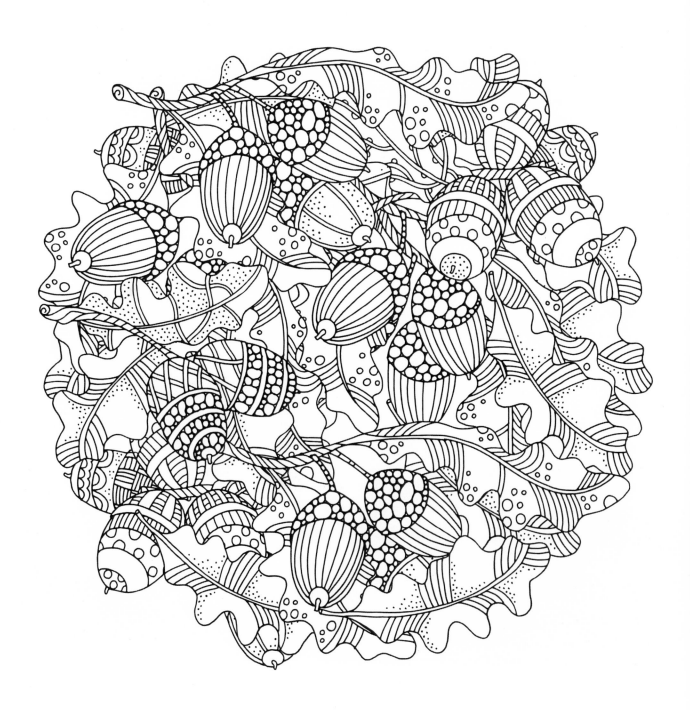

Or Color Outside the Lines!

Date:_____

What can you harvest today in your outdoor garden or the garden in your mind?

This Week's Affirmation (say it out loud)
The older I am, the stronger I become in mind and body.

What is my Intention for the Day?

Consider using the intention list or a tarot or wisdom card. Your daily card might reflect a feeling, an intention, an opportunity, or a gift that you might not have thought of which gives you greater insight.

_____
_____

Question for the Day

How do I feel when someone shares that they have a different experience than me of the same thing? How do I react or respond?

_____
_____

Today I am feeling ...

Name or identify my feelings. Refer back to <u>feeling list</u> if needed.

_____
_____

What is the sensation of that feeling in my body? See <u>sensation list</u>.

_____

What situation or thoughts triggered this feeling?

_____
_____

What is this feeling telling me about what I need in this situation?

_____
_____

I am grateful for:

_____   _____
_____   _____

Daily Focus Planner

Write down three or more things or areas to focus on today that are meaningful.
Prioritize and take action!

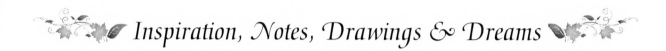 *Inspiration, Notes, Drawings & Dreams*

What happened today that helped me feel more connected to nature?

What had meaning for me today? What do I keep ignoring?

*Date:*_____

Touch the earth today.

This Week's Affirmation (say it out loud)
The older I am, the stronger I become in mind and body.

What is my Intention for the Day?

Consider using the intention list or a tarot or wisdom card. Your daily card might reflect a feeling, an intention, an opportunity, or a gift that you might not have thought of which gives you greater insight.

Question for the Day
What prosperity principles or core values and beliefs do I see supporting me?

Today I am feeling ...
Name or identify my feelings. Refer back to feeling list if needed.

What is the sensation of that feeling in my body? See sensation list.

What situation or thoughts triggered this feeling?

What is this feeling telling me about what I need in this situation?

I am grateful for:

48

Daily Focus Planner

Write down three or more things or areas to focus on today that are meaningful.
Prioritize and take action!

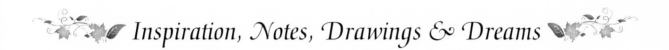 *Inspiration, Notes, Drawings & Dreams*

What happened today that helped me feel more connected to nature?

What had meaning for me today? What do I keep ignoring?

Date:_____

Feel the wind blowing on your face.

This Week's Affirmation (say it out loud)
The older I am, the stronger I become in mind and body.

What is my Intention for the Day?

Consider using the intention list or a tarot or wisdom card. Your daily card might reflect a feeling, an intention, an opportunity, or a gift that you might not have thought of which gives you greater insight.

_____

_____

_____

Question for the Day

› What have I seen this season that has shown me my ability to manifest prosperity in any form?

_____

_____

_____

Today I am feeling …
Name or identify my feelings. Refer back to <u>feeling list</u> if needed.

_____

_____

_____

What is the sensation of that feeling in my body? See <u>sensation list</u>.

_____

What situation or thoughts triggered this feeling?

_____

_____

What is this feeling telling me about what I need in this situation?

_____

_____

_____

I am grateful for:

_____   _____

_____   _____

Daily Focus Planner

Write down three or more things or areas to focus on today that are meaningful.
Prioritize and take action!

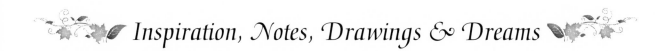 *Inspiration, Notes, Drawings & Dreams*

What happened today that helped me feel more connected to nature?

What had meaning for me today? What do I keep ignoring?

Date:_____

What smells do you notice this season?

This Week's Affirmation (say it out loud)
The older I am, the stronger I become in mind and body.

What is my Intention for the Day?

Consider using the intention list or a tarot or wisdom card. Your daily card might reflect a feeling, an intention, an opportunity, or a gift that you might not have thought of which gives you greater insight.

_____

_____

_____

Question for the Day

What can I do to improve my most important relationships?

_____

_____

_____

Today I am feeling ...

Name or identify my feelings. Refer back to <u>feeling list</u> if needed.

_____

_____

_____

What is the sensation of that feeling in my body? See <u>sensation list</u>.

_____

What situation or thoughts triggered this feeling?

_____

_____

What is this feeling telling me about what I need in this situation?

_____

_____

I am grateful for:

_____   _____

_____   _____

Daily Focus Planner

Write down three or more things or areas to focus on today that are meaningful.
Prioritize and take action!

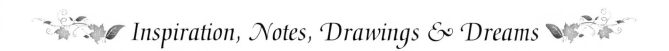 *Inspiration, Notes, Drawings & Dreams*

What happened today that helped me feel more connected to nature?

What had meaning for me today? What do I keep ignoring?

Date:_____

What are the trees doing around you?

This Week's Affirmation (say it out loud)
The older I am, the stronger I become in mind and body.

What is my Intention for the Day?

Consider using the intention list or a tarot or wisdom card. Your daily card might reflect a feeling, an intention, an opportunity, or a gift that you might not have thought of which gives you greater insight.

_____

_____

Question for the Day

How do I want my relationship with myself to look?

_____

_____

Today I am feeling …

Name or identify my feelings. Refer back to <u>feeling list</u> if needed.

_____

_____

What is the sensation of that feeling in my body? See <u>sensation list</u>.

What situation or thoughts triggered this feeling?

_____

What is this feeling telling me about what I need in this situation?

_____

_____

I am grateful for:

_____

_____

Daily Focus Planner

Write down three or more things or areas to focus on today that are meaningful.
Prioritize and take action!

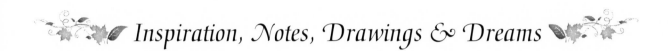 *Inspiration, Notes, Drawings & Dreams*

What happened today that helped me feel more connected to nature?

What had meaning for me today? What do I keep ignoring?

Date:_____

Look up at the sky, what do you see?

This Week's Affirmation (say it out loud)
The older I am, the stronger I become in mind and body.

What is my Intention for the Day?

Consider using the intention list or a tarot or wisdom card. Your daily card might reflect a feeling, an intention, an opportunity, or a gift that you might not have thought of which gives you greater insight.

_____

_____

_____

Question for the Day
What can I think, say, or do today to build my own self-confidence?

_____

_____

_____

Today I am feeling ...
Name or identify my feelings. Refer back to feeling list if needed.

_____

_____

What is the sensation of that feeling in my body? See sensation list.

_____

What situation or thoughts triggered this feeling?

_____

_____

What is this feeling telling me about what I need in this situation?

_____

_____

I am grateful for:

_____

_____

Daily Focus Planner

Write down three or more things or areas to focus on today that are meaningful.
Prioritize and take action!

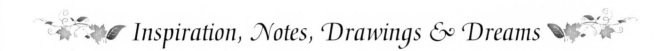 *Inspiration, Notes, Drawings & Dreams*

What happened today that helped me feel more connected to nature?

What had meaning for me today? What do I keep ignoring?

Date:_____

What is the weather like today?

This Week's Affirmation (say it out loud)
I radiate peace and serenity with a smile on my face.

What is my Intention for the Day?

Consider using the intention list or a tarot or wisdom card. Your daily card might reflect a feeling, an intention, an opportunity, or a gift that you might not have thought of which gives you greater insight.

Question for the Day

What excuse do I still use to stop myself from moving ahead in my life? How can I replace this excuse with a clear, positive intention?

Today I am feeling …
Name or identify my feelings. Refer back to <u>feeling list</u> if needed.

What is the sensation of that feeling in my body? See <u>sensation list</u>.

What situation or thoughts triggered this feeling?

What is this feeling telling me about what I need in this situation?

I am grateful for:

58

Weekly Reflections and Inspiration

Use this space to explore your thoughts, readings or other experiences.
For example,

- What did I do this week that was meaningful?
- What were the thoughts, wisdom cards, or readings that captured my heart this week?
- How did nature reflect back to me something about myself?
- What ideas or inspirations do I want to explore further?

What are some empowering steps for next week?

Coloring Meditation

Or Color Outside the Lines!

Date:_____

What can you do in the garden today?

This Week's Affirmation (say it out loud)
I radiate peace and serenity with a smile on my face.

What is my Intention for the Day?

Consider using the intention list or a tarot or wisdom card. Your daily card might reflect a feeling, an intention, an opportunity, or a gift that you might not have thought of which gives you greater insight.

Question for the Day

How do I spend my free time? Does this feel supportive of my physical, mental, emotional, or spiritual well-being? What would feel even more supportive?

Today I am feeling …
Name or identify my feelings. Refer back to <u>feeling list</u> if needed.

What is the sensation of that feeling in my body? See <u>sensation list</u>.

What situation or thoughts triggered this feeling?

What is this feeling telling me about what I need in this situation?

I am grateful for:

Daily Focus Planner

Write down three or more things or areas to focus on today that are meaningful.
Prioritize and take action!

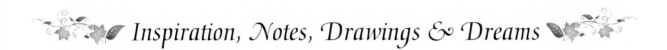 *Inspiration, Notes, Drawings & Dreams*

What happened today that helped me feel more connected to nature?

What had meaning for me today? What do I keep ignoring?

Date:_____

What is something special you have found outdoors?

This Week's Affirmation (say it out loud)
I radiate peace and serenity with a smile on my face.

What is my Intention for the Day?

Consider using the intention list or a tarot or wisdom card. Your daily card might reflect a feeling, an intention, an opportunity, or a gift that you might not have thought of which gives you greater insight.

Question for the Day
What physical exercise would feel good for my body and soul?

Today I am feeling …
Name or identify my feelings. Refer back to <u>feeling list</u> if needed.

What is the sensation of that feeling in my body? See <u>sensation list</u>.

What situation or thoughts triggered this feeling?

What is this feeling telling me about what I need in this situation?

I am grateful for:

Daily Focus Planner

Write down three or more things or areas to focus on today that are meaningful.
Prioritize and take action!

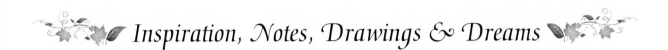 *Inspiration, Notes, Drawings & Dreams*

What happened today that helped me feel more connected to nature?

What had meaning for me today? What do I keep ignoring?

Date:_____

What does it feel like to walk in nature today?

This Week's Affirmation (say it out loud)
I radiate peace and serenity with a smile on my face.

What is my Intention for the Day?

Consider using the intention list or a tarot or wisdom card. Your daily card might reflect a feeling, an intention, an opportunity, or a gift that you might not have thought of which gives you greater insight.

Question for the Day

Where am I wanting greater support for my spiritual awareness and growth? How can I get it?

Today I am feeling …

Name or identify my feelings. Refer back to feeling list if needed.

What is the sensation of that feeling in my body? See sensation list.

What situation or thoughts triggered this feeling?

What is this feeling telling me about what I need in this situation?

I am grateful for:

66

Daily Focus Planner

Write down three or more things or areas to focus on today that are meaningful.
Prioritize and take action!

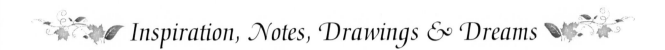 *Inspiration, Notes, Drawings & Dreams*

What happened today that helped me feel more connected to nature?

What had meaning for me today? What do I keep ignoring?

Date:_____

How can you be in the sun today?

This Week's Affirmation (say it out loud)
I radiate peace and serenity with a smile on my face.

What is my Intention for the Day?

Consider using the intention list or a tarot or wisdom card. Your daily card might reflect a feeling, an intention, an opportunity, or a gift that you might not have thought of which gives you greater insight.

_____

_____

Question for the Day

How can I deepen my empathy and compassion? Who or what can I express this part of myself with?

_____

_____

Today I am feeling …

Name or identify my feelings. Refer back to <u>feeling list</u> if needed.

_____

_____

What is the sensation of that feeling in my body? See <u>sensation list</u>.

What situation or thoughts triggered this feeling?

_____

What is this feeling telling me about what I need in this situation?

_____

_____

I am grateful for:

_____   _____

_____   _____

Daily Focus Planner

Write down three or more things or areas to focus on today that are meaningful.
Prioritize and take action!

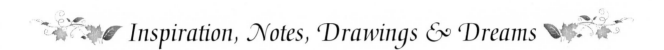 *Inspiration, Notes, Drawings & Dreams*

What happened today that helped me feel more connected to nature?

What had meaning for me today? What do I keep ignoring?

Date:_____

Can you feel the temperature changing? What do you notice?

Physical Activity

This Week's Affirmation (say it out loud)
I radiate peace and serenity with a smile on my face.

What is my Intention for the Day?

Consider using the intention list or a tarot or wisdom card. Your daily card might reflect a feeling, an intention, an opportunity, or a gift that you might not have thought of which gives you greater insight.

_____

_____

_____

Question for the Day

When I lack self-confidence, what messages am I telling myself? What is one thing I can do to change those messages and build my confidence?

_____

_____

_____

Today I am feeling …
Name or identify my feelings. Refer back to <u>feeling list</u> if needed.

_____

_____

_____

What is the sensation of that feeling in my body? See <u>sensation list</u>.

_____

What situation or thoughts triggered this feeling?

_____

_____

_____

What is this feeling telling me about what I need in this situation?

_____

_____

_____

I am grateful for:

_____   _____

_____   _____

_____

70

Daily Focus Planner

Write down three or more things or areas to focus on today that are meaningful.
Prioritize and take action!

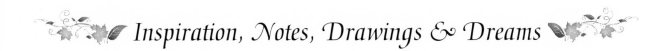 *Inspiration, Notes, Drawings & Dreams*

What happened today that helped me feel more connected to nature?

What had meaning for me today? What do I keep ignoring?

*Date:*_____

What animal shows you freedom?

This Week's Affirmation (say it out loud)
I radiate peace and serenity with a smile on my face.

What is my Intention for the Day?

Consider using the intention list or a tarot or wisdom card. Your daily card might reflect a feeling, an intention, an opportunity, or a gift that you might not have thought of which gives you greater insight.

_____

_____

Question for the Day

Do I have the habit of apologizing to others too much? If so, what's behind that habit and how can I change it?

_____

_____

Today I am feeling …

Name or identify my feelings. Refer back to feeling list if needed.

_____

_____

What is the sensation of that feeling in my body? See sensation list.

_____

What situation or thoughts triggered this feeling?

_____

_____

What is this feeling telling me about what I need in this situation?

_____

_____

I am grateful for:

_____   _____

_____   _____

Daily Focus Planner

Write down three or more things or areas to focus on today that are meaningful.
Prioritize and take action!

 *Inspiration, Notes, Drawings & Dreams*

What happened today that helped me feel more connected to nature?

What had meaning for me today? What do I keep ignoring?

Date:_____

What plant helps you to smile today?

This Week's Affirmation (say it out loud)
I enjoy foods that feed and support every cell of my body.

What is my Intention for the Day?

Consider using the intention list or a tarot or wisdom card. Your daily card might reflect a feeling, an intention, an opportunity, or a gift that you might not have thought of which gives you greater insight.

Question for the Day

How can I support others and our world with what I have?

Today I am feeling ...
Name or identify my feelings. Refer back to <u>feeling list</u> if needed.

What is the sensation of that feeling in my body? See <u>sensation list</u>.

What situation or thoughts triggered this feeling?

What is this feeling telling me about what I need in this situation?

I am grateful for:

74

Weekly Reflections and Inspiration

Use this space to explore your thoughts, readings or other experiences.
For example,

- What did I do this week that was meaningful?
- What were the thoughts, wisdom cards, or readings that captured my heart this week?
- How did nature reflect back to me something about myself?
- What ideas or inspirations do I want to explore further?

Coloring Meditation

Or Color Outside the Lines!

Date:_____

How is the Divine Goddess or God showing her or himself to you?

This Week's Affirmation (say it out loud)
I enjoy foods that feed and support every cell of my body.

What is my Intention for the Day?

Consider using the intention list or a tarot or wisdom card. Your daily card might reflect a feeling, an intention, an opportunity, or a gift that you might not have thought of which gives you greater insight.

Question for the Day

How do my prosperity beliefs impact my relationships? How do I let my partner/friends impact me with theirs? Is there anything I might want to shift regarding this? If so, what?

Today I am feeling …
Name or identify my feelings. Refer back to feeling list if needed.

What is the sensation of that feeling in my body? See sensation list.

What situation or thoughts triggered this feeling?

What is this feeling telling me about what I need in this situation?

I am grateful for:

Daily Focus Planner

Write down three or more things or areas to focus on today that are meaningful.
Prioritize and take action!

 *Inspiration, Notes, Drawings & Dreams*

What happened today that helped me feel more connected to nature?

What had meaning for me today? What do I keep ignoring?

Date:_____

What is the light doing differently now?

This Week's Affirmation (say it out loud)
I enjoy foods that feed and support every cell of my body.

What is my Intention for the Day?

Consider using the intention list or a tarot or wisdom card. Your daily card might reflect a feeling, an intention, an opportunity, or a gift that you might not have thought of which gives you greater insight.

_____
_____
_____

Question for the Day

How is my relationship to Nature expanding or deepening?

_____
_____
_____

Today I am feeling ...
Name or identify my feelings. Refer back to <u>feeling list</u> if needed.

_____
_____
_____

What is the sensation of that feeling in my body? See <u>sensation list</u>.

_____

What situation or thoughts triggered this feeling?

_____
_____

What is this feeling telling me about what I need in this situation?

_____
_____
_____

I am grateful for:

_____   _____
_____   _____

Daily Focus Planner

Write down three or more things or areas to focus on today that are meaningful.
Prioritize and take action!

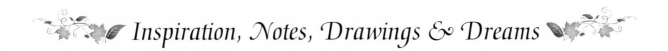 *Inspiration, Notes, Drawings & Dreams*

What happened today that helped me feel more connected to nature?

What had meaning for me today? What do I keep ignoring?

*Date:*_____

Sit near the roots of some precious trees.

This Week's Affirmation (say it out loud)
I enjoy foods that feed and support every cell of my body.

What is my Intention for the Day?

Consider using the intention list or a tarot or wisdom card. Your daily card might reflect a feeling, an intention, an opportunity, or a gift that you might not have thought of which gives you greater insight.

Question for the Day
In what areas of my life can I show greater loving kindness toward myself? What will I do to begin today?

Today I am feeling …
Name or identify my feelings. Refer back to <u>feeling list</u> if needed.

What is the sensation of that feeling in my body? See <u>sensation list</u>.

What situation or thoughts triggered this feeling?

What is this feeling telling me about what I need in this situation?

I am grateful for:

82

Daily Focus Planner

Write down three or more things or areas to focus on today that are meaningful.
Prioritize and take action!

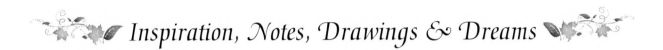 *Inspiration, Notes, Drawings & Dreams*

What happened today that helped me feel more connected to nature?

What had meaning for me today? What do I keep ignoring?

Date:_____

Look outside tonight and see the moon shining on a tree or a bush.

This Week's Affirmation (say it out loud)
I enjoy foods that feed and support every cell of my body.

What is my Intention for the Day?

Consider using the intention list or a tarot or wisdom card. Your daily card might reflect a feeling, an intention, an opportunity, or a gift that you might not have thought of which gives you greater insight.

_____

_____

_____

Question for the Day
What are my strengths, gifts, and talents? (Name at least one of each.)

_____

_____

_____

Today I am feeling …
Name or identify my feelings. Refer back to <u>feeling list</u> if needed.

_____

_____

_____

What is the sensation of that feeling in my body? See <u>sensation list</u>.

_____

What situation or thoughts triggered this feeling?

_____

_____

What is this feeling telling me about what I need in this situation?

_____

_____

_____

I am grateful for:

_____   _____

_____   _____

Daily Focus Planner

Write down three or more things or areas to focus on today that are meaningful.
Prioritize and take action!

 *Inspiration, Notes, Drawings & Dreams*

What happened today that helped me feel more connected to nature?

What had meaning for me today? What do I keep ignoring?

Date:_____

Give a blessing to the sky today

This Week's Affirmation (say it out loud)
I enjoy foods that feed and support every cell of my body.

What is my Intention for the Day?

Consider using the intention list or a tarot or wisdom card. Your daily card might reflect a feeling, an intention, an opportunity, or a gift that you might not have thought of which gives you greater insight.

Question for the Day

What foods do I notice I crave? What foods do I know I really need to support my body as a sacred temple?

Today I am feeling …
Name or identify my feelings. Refer back to feeling list if needed.

What is the sensation of that feeling in my body? See sensation list.

What situation or thoughts triggered this feeling?

What is this feeling telling me about what I need in this situation?

I am grateful for:

Daily Focus Planner

Write down three or more things or areas to focus on today that are meaningful.
Prioritize and take action!

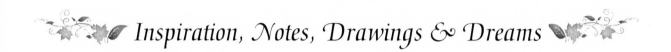 *Inspiration, Notes, Drawings & Dreams*

What happened today that helped me feel more connected to nature?

What had meaning for me today? What do I keep ignoring?

Date:_____

How might you honor the ancestors who walked before you?

This Week's Affirmation (say it out loud)
I enjoy foods that feed and support every cell of my body.

What is my Intention for the Day?

Consider using the intention list or a tarot or wisdom card. Your daily card might reflect a feeling, an intention, an opportunity, or a gift that you might not have thought of which gives you greater insight.

_____

_____

Question for the Day

What emotions do I feel that might trigger me to eat or not eat? Who can I pray for, bless, or express compassion for in my circle of friends or for myself?

_____

_____

Today I am feeling …
Name or identify my feelings. Refer back to <u>feeling list</u> if needed.

_____

_____

What is the sensation of that feeling in my body? See <u>sensation list</u>.

_____

What situation or thoughts triggered this feeling?

_____

_____

What is this feeling telling me about what I need in this situation?

_____

_____

I am grateful for:

_____

_____

Daily Focus Planner

Write down three or more things or areas to focus on today that are meaningful.
Prioritize and take action!

 *Inspiration, Notes, Drawings & Dreams*

What happened today that helped me feel more connected to nature?

What had meaning for me today? What do I keep ignoring?

Date:_____

What do you see tonight that stands out for you?

This Week's Affirmation (say it out loud)
I continue to learn new ways to support my mind, body, and spirit.

What is my Intention for the Day?

Consider using the intention list or a tarot or wisdom card. Your daily card might reflect a feeling, an intention, an opportunity, or a gift that you might not have thought of which gives you greater insight.

_____

_____

Question for the Day

How can I be a gift of light and love in my greater community? What would feel easy and good to do? What might be challenging but gratifying?

_____

_____

Today I am feeling …
Name or identify my feelings. Refer back to feeling list if needed.

_____

_____

What is the sensation of that feeling in my body? See sensation list.

_____

What situation or thoughts triggered this feeling?

_____

_____

What is this feeling telling me about what I need in this situation?

_____

_____

I am grateful for:

_____   _____

_____   _____

90

Weekly Reflections and Inspiration

Use this space to explore your thoughts, readings or other experiences.
For example,

- What did I do this week that was meaningful?
- What were the thoughts, wisdom cards, or readings that captured my heart this week?
- How did nature reflect back to me something about myself?
- What ideas or inspirations do I want to explore further?

What are some empowering steps for next week?

Coloring Meditation

Or Color Outside the Lines!

Date:_____

Where is a shelter of trees or bushes that you can find to sit under?

This Week's Affirmation (say it out loud)
I continue to learn new ways to support my mind, body, and spirit.

What is my Intention for the Day?
Consider using the intention list or a tarot or wisdom card. Your daily card might reflect a feeling, an intention, an opportunity, or a gift that you might not have thought of which gives you greater insight.

_____

_____

Question for the Day
In terms of my emotional behavior, how would I describe myself?

_____

_____

Today I am feeling …
Name or identify my feelings. Refer back to <u>feeling list</u> if needed.

_____

_____

What is the sensation of that feeling in my body? See <u>sensation list</u>.

_____

What situation or thoughts triggered this feeling?

_____

_____

What is this feeling telling me about what I need in this situation?

_____

_____

I am grateful for:

_____

_____

Daily Focus Planner

Write down three or more things or areas to focus on today that are meaningful.
Prioritize and take action!

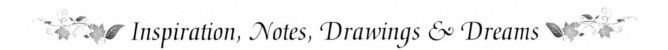 *Inspiration, Notes, Drawings & Dreams*

What happened today that helped me feel more connected to nature?

What had meaning for me today? What do I keep ignoring?

Date:_____

Observe the clouds today. What unique clouds showed
themselves to you?

This Week's Affirmation (say it out loud)
I continue to learn new ways to support my mind, body, and spirit.

What is my Intention for the Day?

Consider using the intention list or a tarot or wisdom card. Your daily card might reflect a feeling, an
intention, an opportunity, or a gift that you might not have thought of which gives you greater insight.

_____

_____

Question for the Day

What gets in my way of accepting help or allowing praise? How can I allow others and myself to praise and
support me more fully?

_____

_____

Today I am feeling …
Name or identify my feelings. Refer back to <u>feeling list</u> if needed.

_____

_____

What is the sensation of that feeling in my body? See <u>sensation list</u>.

_____

What situation or thoughts triggered this feeling?

_____

_____

What is this feeling telling me about what I need in this situation?

_____

_____

I am grateful for:

_____   _____

_____   _____

Daily Focus Planner

Write down three or more things or areas to focus on today that are meaningful.
Prioritize and take action!

 *Inspiration, Notes, Drawings & Dreams*

What happened today that helped me feel more connected to nature?

What had meaning for me today? What do I keep ignoring?

Date:_____

Look at the stars tonight. Are they twinkling?

This Week's Affirmation (say it out loud)
I continue to learn new ways to support my mind, body, and spirit.

What is my Intention for the Day?

Consider using the intention list or a tarot or wisdom card. Your daily card might reflect a feeling, an intention, an opportunity, or a gift that you might not have thought of which gives you greater insight.

_____

_____

_____

Question for the Day
How do I want my relationships with others to look?

_____

_____

_____

Today I am feeling …
Name or identify my feelings. Refer back to <u>feeling list</u> if needed.

_____

_____

_____

What is the sensation of that feeling in my body? See <u>sensation list</u>.

_____

What situation or thoughts triggered this feeling?

_____

_____

What is this feeling telling me about what I need in this situation?

_____

_____

_____

I am grateful for:

_____ _____

_____ _____

Monthly Reflections and Renewal

Review the five aspects of well-being. What aspect(s) of Physical, Relational, Mental, Spiritual and Financial and Career are showing up in my life this month?

_____
_____
_____
_____

How are my passions and actions moving me closer to living a fuller and more engaged life?

_____
_____
_____
_____

Am I happy with the results and feeling this brings to me?

_____
_____
_____
_____

What is or is not showing up for each aspect of well-being? Why might that be?

_____
_____
_____
_____

What would I change for next month so that I can gently course-correct and take actions that support me? Listen gently to what I am saying…

_____
_____
_____

Notes

You can find a calendar showing the phases of the moon and other notable astronomical events at **www.seasonalwidomjournal.com/calendar.**

Print the calendar, trim it to fit, and then paste it onto this page.

November

Sunday	Monday	Tuesday	Wednesday	Thursday	Friday	Saturday

Date:_____

Can you find a wild place in your yard?

This Week's Affirmation (say it out loud)
I continue to learn new ways to support my mind, body, and spirit.

What is my Intention for the Day?

Consider using the intention list or a tarot or wisdom card. Your daily card might reflect a feeling, an intention, an opportunity, or a gift that you might not have thought of which gives you greater insight.

_____

_____

Question for the Day

When am I my most inspired self? And when do I feel disempowered?

_____

_____

Today I am feeling ...

Name or identify my feelings. Refer back to <u>feeling list</u> if needed.

_____

_____

What is the sensation of that feeling in my body? See <u>sensation list</u>.

_____

What situation or thoughts triggered this feeling?

_____

_____

What is this feeling telling me about what I need in this situation?

_____

_____

I am grateful for:

_____

_____

Daily Focus Planner

Write down three or more things or areas to focus on today that are meaningful.
Prioritize and take action!

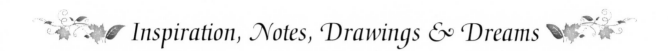 *Inspiration, Notes, Drawings & Dreams*

What happened today that helped me feel more connected to nature?

What had meaning for me today? What do I keep ignoring?

*Date:*_____

How do you feel after breathing in some fresh air?

This Week's Affirmation (say it out loud)
I continue to learn new ways to support my mind, body, and spirit.

What is my Intention for the Day?

Consider using the intention list or a tarot or wisdom card. Your daily card might reflect a feeling, an intention, an opportunity, or a gift that you might not have thought of which gives you greater insight.

Question for the Day

When I notice an addictive pattern within myself, with food, social media, or other obsessions, what can I forgive myself for?

Today I am feeling …
Name or identify my feelings. Refer back to <u>feeling list</u> if needed.

What is the sensation of that feeling in my body? See <u>sensation list</u>.

What situation or thoughts triggered this feeling?

What is this feeling telling me about what I need in this situation?

I am grateful for:

Daily Focus Planner

Write down three or more things or areas to focus on today that are meaningful.
Prioritize and take action!

 *Inspiration, Notes, Drawings & Dreams*

What happened today that helped me feel more connected to nature?

What had meaning for me today? What do I keep ignoring?

*Date:*_____

What is showing up for you by taking a walk today?

This Week's Affirmation (say it out loud)
My love for myself grows and I become a better friend to my body.

What is my Intention for the Day?

Consider using the intention list or a tarot or wisdom card. Your daily card might reflect a feeling, an intention, an opportunity, or a gift that you might not have thought of which gives you greater insight.

Question for the Day
Who could I do something nice for today? What will I do?

Today I am feeling ...
Name or identify my feelings. Refer back to <u>feeling list</u> if needed.

What is the sensation of that feeling in my body? See <u>sensation list</u>.

What situation or thoughts triggered this feeling?

What is this feeling telling me about what I need in this situation?

I am grateful for:

Weekly Reflections and Inspiration

Use this space to explore your thoughts, readings or other experiences.
For example,

- What did I do this week that was meaningful?
- What were the thoughts, wisdom cards, or readings that captured my heart this week?
- How did nature reflect back to me something about myself?
- What ideas or inspirations do I want to explore further?

What are some empowering steps for next week?

Coloring Meditation

Or Color Outside the Lines!

*Date:*_____

Explore sensations when sitting outside today.

This Week's Affirmation (say it out loud)
My love for myself grows and I become a better friend to my body.

What is my Intention for the Day?

Consider using the intention list or a tarot or wisdom card. Your daily card might reflect a feeling, an intention, an opportunity, or a gift that you might not have thought of which gives you greater insight.

Question for the Day
List 3 - 5 things outdoors, or connected to being outdoors, that bring me joy.

Today I am feeling …
Name or identify my feelings. Refer back to <u>feeling list</u> if needed.

What is the sensation of that feeling in my body? See <u>sensation list</u>.

What situation or thoughts triggered this feeling?

What is this feeling telling me about what I need in this situation?

I am grateful for:

110

Daily Focus Planner

Write down three or more things or areas to focus on today that are meaningful.
Prioritize and take action!

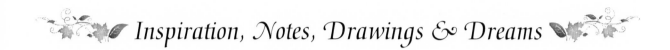 *Inspiration, Notes, Drawings & Dreams*

What happened today that helped me feel more connected to nature?

What had meaning for me today? What do I keep ignoring?

Date:_____

Really look at a leaf today. What do you notice?

This Week's Affirmation (say it out loud)
My love for myself grows and I become a better friend to my body.

What is my Intention for the Day?

Consider using the intention list or a tarot or wisdom card. Your daily card might reflect a feeling, an intention, an opportunity, or a gift that you might not have thought of which gives you greater insight.

_____

_____

_____

Question for the Day
What animal or plant gives me a sense of peace and joy to be around?

_____

_____

_____

Today I am feeling …
Name or identify my feelings. Refer back to <u>feeling list</u> if needed.

_____

_____

_____

What is the sensation of that feeling in my body? See <u>sensation list</u>.

_____

_____

What situation or thoughts triggered this feeling?

_____

_____

What is this feeling telling me about what I need in this situation?

_____

_____

_____

I am grateful for:

_____   _____

_____   _____

Daily Focus Planner

Write down three or more things or areas to focus on today that are meaningful.
Prioritize and take action!

 *Inspiration, Notes, Drawings & Dreams*

What happened today that helped me feel more connected to nature?

What had meaning for me today? What do I keep ignoring?

*Date:*_____

What kinds of clouds do you see?

This Week's Affirmation (say it out loud)
My love for myself grows and I become a better friend to my body.

What is my Intention for the Day?

Consider using the intention list or a tarot or wisdom card. Your daily card might reflect a feeling, an intention, an opportunity, or a gift that you might not have thought of which gives you greater insight.

_____
_____

Question for the Day

What are some fun things I enjoy doing to unwind and de-stress?

_____
_____
_____

Today I am feeling ...

Name or identify my feelings. Refer back to <u>feeling list</u> if needed.

_____
_____
_____

What is the sensation of that feeling in my body? See <u>sensation list</u>.

What situation or thoughts triggered this feeling?

_____
_____

What is this feeling telling me about what I need in this situation?

_____
_____
_____

I am grateful for:

_____
_____
_____

114

Daily Focus Planner

Write down three or more things or areas to focus on today that are meaningful.
Prioritize and take action!

Inspiration, Notes, Drawings & Dreams

What happened today that helped me feel more connected to nature?

What had meaning for me today? What do I keep ignoring?

*Date:*_____

Study a branch, what is it showing you?

This Week's Affirmation (say it out loud)
My love for myself grows and I become a better friend to my body.

What is my Intention for the Day?

Consider using the intention list or a tarot or wisdom card. Your daily card might reflect a feeling, an intention, an opportunity, or a gift that you might not have thought of which gives you greater insight.

_____

_____

_____

Question for the Day

What have I done this season that has made a difference in my life and that of others?

_____

_____

_____

Today I am feeling …

Name or identify my feelings. Refer back to <u>feeling list</u> if needed.

_____

_____

_____

What is the sensation of that feeling in my body? See <u>sensation list</u>.

_____

What situation or thoughts triggered this feeling?

_____

_____

What is this feeling telling me about what I need in this situation?

_____

_____

_____

I am grateful for:

_____   _____

_____   _____

116

Daily Focus Planner

Write down three or more things or areas to focus on today that are meaningful.
Prioritize and take action!

 *Inspiration, Notes, Drawings & Dreams*

What happened today that helped me feel more connected to nature?

What had meaning for me today? What do I keep ignoring?

*Date:*_____

Watch the sunset tonight

This Week's Affirmation (say it out loud)
My love for myself grows and I become a better friend to my body.

What is my Intention for the Day?

Consider using the intention list or a tarot or wisdom card. Your daily card might reflect a feeling, an intention, an opportunity, or a gift that you might not have thought of which gives you greater insight.

_____

_____

Question for the Day

Who are the people in my inner circle I trust. What do they do that feels supportive? Why is this important to me?

_____

_____

Today I am feeling …

Name or identify my feelings. Refer back to <u>feeling list</u> if needed.

_____

_____

What is the sensation of that feeling in my body? See <u>sensation list</u>.

_____

What situation or thoughts triggered this feeling?

_____

_____

What is this feeling telling me about what I need in this situation?

_____

_____

I am grateful for:

_____   _____

_____   _____

Daily Focus Planner

Write down three or more things or areas to focus on today that are meaningful.
Prioritize and take action!

Inspiration, Notes, Drawings & Dreams

What happened today that helped me feel more connected to nature?

What had meaning for me today? What do I keep ignoring?

*Date:*_____

Give thanks to the sun today

This Week's Affirmation (say it out loud)
My love for myself grows and I become a better friend to my body.

What is my Intention for the Day?

Consider using the intention list or a tarot or wisdom card. Your daily card might reflect a feeling, an intention, an opportunity, or a gift that you might not have thought of which gives you greater insight.

Question for the Day

When I feel emotionally charged, shut down or contracted, what supports me to relax and calm down in order to feel more connected and be able to communicate more constructively with others?

Today I am feeling …
Name or identify my feelings. Refer back to <u>feeling list</u> if needed.

What is the sensation of that feeling in my body? See <u>sensation list</u>.

What situation or thoughts triggered this feeling?

What is this feeling telling me about what I need in this situation?

I am grateful for:

Daily Focus Planner

Write down three or more things or areas to focus on today that are meaningful.
Prioritize and take action!

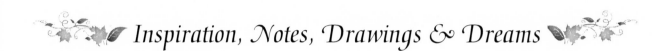 *Inspiration, Notes, Drawings & Dreams*

What happened today that helped me feel more connected to nature?

What had meaning for me today? What do I keep ignoring?

Date:_____

Explore playing outdoors. What will you do?

This Week's Affirmation (say it out loud)
I eat nutritious foods and drink plenty of water to feed and cleanse my body.

What is my Intention for the Day?

Consider using the intention list or a tarot or wisdom card. Your daily card might reflect a feeling, an intention, an opportunity, or a gift that you might not have thought of which gives you greater insight.

_____
_____

Question for the Day

What values do I have that support my career and my prosperity? What values do I have that might be working against my prosperity?

_____
_____

Today I am feeling …

Name or identify my feelings. Refer back to <u>feeling list</u> if needed.

_____
_____

What is the sensation of that feeling in my body? See <u>sensation list</u>.

_____

What situation or thoughts triggered this feeling?

_____
_____

What is this feeling telling me about what I need in this situation?

_____
_____

I am grateful for:

_____ | _____
_____ | _____

Weekly Reflections and Inspiration

Use this space to explore your thoughts, readings or other experiences.
For example,

- What did I do this week that was meaningful?
- What were the thoughts, wisdom cards, or readings that captured my heart this week?
- How did nature reflect back to me something about myself?
- What ideas or inspirations do I want to explore further?

What are some empowering steps for next week?

Coloring Meditation

Or Color Outside the Lines!

Date:_____

Dark skies—go out there and enjoy!

This Week's Affirmation (say it out loud)
I eat nutritious foods and drink plenty of water to feed and cleanse my body.

What is my Intention for the Day?

Consider using the intention list or a tarot or wisdom card. Your daily card might reflect a feeling, an intention, an opportunity, or a gift that you might not have thought of which gives you greater insight.

Question for the Day

What do I see as my lifestyle and standard of living now? Is there anything I'd like to change? What is one step I could take?

Today I am feeling …
Name or identify my feelings. Refer back to feeling list if needed.

What is the sensation of that feeling in my body? See sensation list.

What situation or thoughts triggered this feeling?

What is this feeling telling me about what I need in this situation?

I am grateful for:

126

Daily Focus Planner

Write down three or more things or areas to focus on today that are meaningful.
Prioritize and take action!

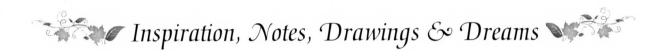 *Inspiration, Notes, Drawings & Dreams*

What happened today that helped me feel more connected to nature?

What had meaning for me today? What do I keep ignoring?

Date:_____

What insect can you find today? What adventure was it on?

This Week's Affirmation (say it out loud)
I eat nutritious foods and drink plenty of water to feed and cleanse my body.

What is my Intention for the Day?
Consider using the intention list or a tarot or wisdom card. Your daily card might reflect a feeling, an intention, an opportunity, or a gift that you might not have thought of which gives you greater insight.

Question for the Day
Who are the people and relationships that matter most to me now? Why?

Today I am feeling ...
Name or identify my feelings. Refer back to feeling list if needed.

What is the sensation of that feeling in my body? See sensation list.

What situation or thoughts triggered this feeling?

What is this feeling telling me about what I need in this situation?

I am grateful for:

Daily Focus Planner

Write down three or more things or areas to focus on today that are meaningful.
Prioritize and take action!

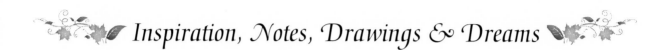 *Inspiration, Notes, Drawings & Dreams*

What happened today that helped me feel more connected to nature?

What had meaning for me today? What do I keep ignoring?

Date:_____

Can you find a moment of peace outside today?

This Week's Affirmation (say it out loud)
I eat nutritious foods and drink plenty of water to feed and cleanse my body.

What is my Intention for the Day?
Consider using the intention list or a tarot or wisdom card. Your daily card might reflect a feeling, an intention, an opportunity, or a gift that you might not have thought of which gives you greater insight.

_____

_____

Question for the Day
➹ What's the next step into my future self that would feel really good?

_____

_____

Today I am feeling ...
Name or identify my feelings. Refer back to feeling list if needed.

_____

_____

What is the sensation of that feeling in my body? See sensation list.

_____

What situation or thoughts triggered this feeling?

_____

What is this feeling telling me about what I need in this situation?

_____

_____

I am grateful for:

_____   _____

_____   _____

Daily Focus Planner

Write down three or more things or areas to focus on today that are meaningful.
Prioritize and take action!

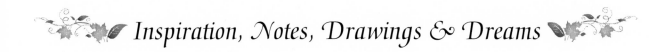 *Inspiration, Notes, Drawings & Dreams*

What happened today that helped me feel more connected to nature?

What had meaning for me today? What do I keep ignoring?

Date:_____

Go outside and look for stars tonight.

This Week's Affirmation (say it out loud)
I eat nutritious foods and drink plenty of water to feed and cleanse my body.

What is my Intention for the Day?
Consider using the intention list or a tarot or wisdom card. Your daily card might reflect a feeling, an intention, an opportunity, or a gift that you might not have thought of which gives you greater insight.

Question for the Day
What can I do today to be kinder to myself and others? How can I continue on this path?

Today I am feeling …
Name or identify my feelings. Refer back to <u>feeling list</u> if needed.

What is the sensation of that feeling in my body? See <u>sensation list</u>.

What situation or thoughts triggered this feeling?

What is this feeling telling me about what I need in this situation?

I am grateful for:

132

Daily Focus Planner

Write down three or more things or areas to focus on today that are meaningful.
Prioritize and take action!

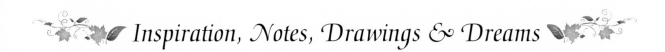 *Inspiration, Notes, Drawings & Dreams*

What happened today that helped me feel more connected to nature?

What had meaning for me today? What do I keep ignoring?

Date:_____

Wake up early and see what the morning is doing.

This Week's Affirmation (say it out loud)
I eat nutritious foods and drink plenty of water to feed and cleanse my body.

What is my Intention for the Day?

Consider using the intention list or a tarot or wisdom card. Your daily card might reflect a feeling, an intention, an opportunity, or a gift that you might not have thought of which gives you greater insight.

_____
_____
_____

Question for the Day

What would be a supportive wellness plan that includes all aspects of my health? Who can help me create it?

_____
_____
_____

Today I am feeling …

Name or identify my feelings. Refer back to feeling list if needed.

_____
_____
_____

What is the sensation of that feeling in my body? See sensation list.

_____

What situation or thoughts triggered this feeling?

_____
_____
_____

What is this feeling telling me about what I need in this situation?

_____
_____
_____

I am grateful for:

_____   _____
_____   _____

Daily Focus Planner

Write down three or more things or areas to focus on today that are meaningful.
Prioritize and take action!

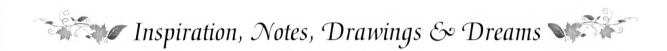 *Inspiration, Notes, Drawings & Dreams*

What happened today that helped me feel more connected to nature?

What had meaning for me today? What do I keep ignoring?

Date:_____

Find a quiet place today and breathe in some oxygen.

This Week's Affirmation (say it out loud)
I eat nutritious foods and drink plenty of water to feed and cleanse my body.

What is my Intention for the Day?

Consider using the intention list or a tarot or wisdom card. Your daily card might reflect a feeling, an intention, an opportunity, or a gift that you might not have thought of which gives you greater insight.

Question for the Day
What is something I appreciate about my body these days?

Today I am feeling …
Name or identify my feelings. Refer back to <u>feeling list</u> if needed.

What is the sensation of that feeling in my body? See <u>sensation list</u>.

What situation or thoughts triggered this feeling?

What is this feeling telling me about what I need in this situation?

I am grateful for:

Daily Focus Planner

Write down three or more things or areas to focus on today that are meaningful.
Prioritize and take action!

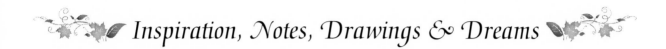 *Inspiration, Notes, Drawings & Dreams*

What happened today that helped me feel more connected to nature?

What had meaning for me today? What do I keep ignoring?

Date:_____

What is different about being outside today?

This Week's Affirmation (say it out loud)
My body is a sacred temple and my inner wisdom shines.

What is my Intention for the Day?

Consider using the intention list or a tarot or wisdom card. Your daily card might reflect a feeling, an intention, an opportunity, or a gift that you might not have thought of which gives you greater insight.

_____

_____

_____

Question for the Day

How does Spirit/God/Nature help and support me to shift my perspective when I need to? What can I do to actively make a shift?

_____

_____

_____

Today I am feeling ...

Name or identify my feelings. Refer back to <u>feeling list</u> if needed.

_____

_____

What is the sensation of that feeling in my body? See <u>sensation list</u>.

_____

What situation or thoughts triggered this feeling?

_____

_____

What is this feeling telling me about what I need in this situation?

_____

_____

I am grateful for:

_____   _____

_____   _____

Weekly Reflections and Inspiration

Use this space to explore your thoughts, readings or other experiences. For example,

- What did I do this week that was meaningful?
- What were the thoughts, wisdom cards, or readings that captured my heart this week?
- How did nature reflect back to me something about myself?
- What ideas or inspirations do I want to explore further?

Coloring Meditation

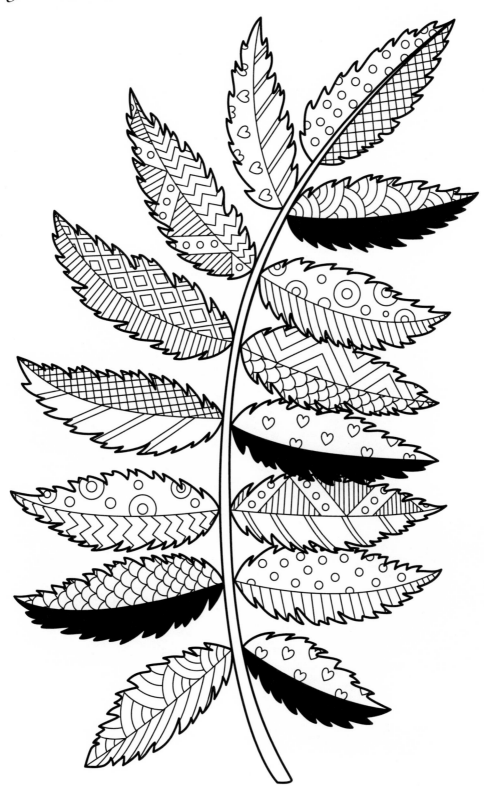

Or Color Outside the Lines!

Date:_____

Listen to the birds today. Why might this make you feel happy?

This Week's Affirmation (say it out loud)
My body is a sacred temple and my inner wisdom shines.

What is my Intention for the Day?

Consider using the intention list or a tarot or wisdom card. Your daily card might reflect a feeling, an intention, an opportunity, or a gift that you might not have thought of which gives you greater insight.

_____

_____

_____

Question for the Day
How is my spirituality connected to self-confidence and self-image?

_____

_____

_____

Today I am feeling …
Name or identify my feelings. Refer back to <u>feeling list</u> if needed.

_____

_____

What is the sensation of that feeling in my body? See <u>sensation list</u>.

_____

What situation or thoughts triggered this feeling?

_____

_____

What is this feeling telling me about what I need in this situation?

_____

_____

I am grateful for:

_____   _____

_____   _____

142

Daily Focus Planner

Write down three or more things or areas to focus on today that are meaningful.
Prioritize and take action!

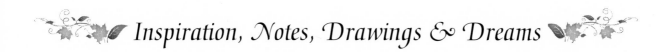 *Inspiration, Notes, Drawings & Dreams*

What happened today that helped me feel more connected to nature?

What had meaning for me today? What do I keep ignoring?

Date:_____

Find an acorn, pinecone, or seed pod. What do you notice?

This Week's Affirmation (say it out loud)
My body is a sacred temple and my inner wisdom shines.

What is my Intention for the Day?
Consider using the intention list or a tarot or wisdom card. Your daily card might reflect a feeling, an intention, an opportunity, or a gift that you might not have thought of which gives you greater insight.

Question for the Day
What helps me to keep going when things get challenging or difficult?

Today I am feeling …
Name or identify my feelings. Refer back to <u>feeling list</u> if needed.

What is the sensation of that feeling in my body? See <u>sensation list</u>.

What situation or thoughts triggered this feeling?

What is this feeling telling me about what I need in this situation?

I am grateful for:

144

Daily Focus Planner

Write down three or more things or areas to focus on today that are meaningful.
Prioritize and take action!

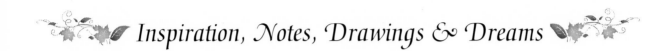 *Inspiration, Notes, Drawings & Dreams*

What happened today that helped me feel more connected to nature?

What had meaning for me today? What do I keep ignoring?

Date:_____

What animals are you not seeing anymore?

This Week's Affirmation (say it out loud)
My body is a sacred temple and my inner wisdom shines.

What is my Intention for the Day?

Consider using the intention list or a tarot or wisdom card. Your daily card might reflect a feeling, an intention, an opportunity, or a gift that you might not have thought of which gives you greater insight.

_____

_____

Question for the Day

What are my dominant feelings these days? How do these feelings erode or support my well-being?

_____

_____

Today I am feeling …
Name or identify my feelings. Refer back to <u>feeling list</u> if needed.

_____

_____

What is the sensation of that feeling in my body? See <u>sensation list</u>.

_____

What situation or thoughts triggered this feeling?

_____

_____

What is this feeling telling me about what I need in this situation?

_____

_____

I am grateful for:

_____   _____

_____   _____

Daily Focus Planner

Write down three or more things or areas to focus on today that are meaningful.
Prioritize and take action!

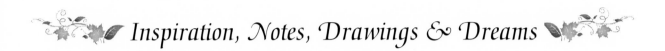 *Inspiration, Notes, Drawings & Dreams*

What happened today that helped me feel more connected to nature?

What had meaning for me today? What do I keep ignoring?

Date:_____

What colors do you see when you look at the earth while walking today?

This Week's Affirmation (say it out loud)
My body is a sacred temple and my inner wisdom shines.

What is my Intention for the Day?

Consider using the intention list or a tarot or wisdom card. Your daily card might reflect a feeling, an intention, an opportunity, or a gift that you might not have thought of which gives you greater insight.

_____

_____

Question for the Day

How much money is enough for me? What am I doing right now to allow that much into my life? What would I need to do to allow more income to come in?

_____

_____

Today I am feeling …
Name or identify my feelings. Refer back to <u>feeling list</u> if needed.

_____

_____

What is the sensation of that feeling in my body? See <u>sensation list</u>.

_____

What situation or thoughts triggered this feeling?

_____

_____

What is this feeling telling me about what I need in this situation?

_____

_____

I am grateful for:

_____

_____

Daily Focus Planner

Write down three or more things or areas to focus on today that are meaningful.
Prioritize and take action!

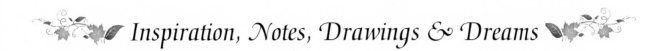 *Inspiration, Notes, Drawings & Dreams*

What happened today that helped me feel more connected to nature?

What had meaning for me today? What do I keep ignoring?

Date:_____

What is happening to the temperature and plants outside now?

This Week's Affirmation (say it out loud)
My body is a sacred temple and my inner wisdom shines.

What is my Intention for the Day?

Consider using the intention list or a tarot or wisdom card. Your daily card might reflect a feeling, an intention, an opportunity, or a gift that you might not have thought of which gives you greater insight.

_____

_____

Question for the Day

Do I see a link between my prosperity and my spiritual beliefs? What is it and how can it be strengthened?

_____

_____

Today I am feeling …

Name or identify my feelings. Refer back to feeling list if needed.

_____

_____

What is the sensation of that feeling in my body? See sensation list.

_____

What situation or thoughts triggered this feeling?

_____

_____

What is this feeling telling me about what I need in this situation?

_____

_____

I am grateful for:

_____

_____

Daily Focus Planner

Write down three or more things or areas to focus on today that are meaningful.
Prioritize and take action!

 *Inspiration, Notes, Drawings & Dreams*

What happened today that helped me feel more connected to nature?

What had meaning for me today? What do I keep ignoring?

*Date:*_____

What are you grateful for when you step outside today?

This Week's Affirmation (say it out loud)
My body is a sacred temple and my inner wisdom shines.

What is my Intention for the Day?

Consider using the intention list or a tarot or wisdom card. Your daily card might reflect a feeling, an intention, an opportunity, or a gift that you might not have thought of which gives you greater insight.

Question for the Day

• With whom do I need to create better boundaries in my life? What could that look like?

Today I am feeling …

Name or identify my feelings. Refer back to <u>feeling list</u> if needed.

What is the sensation of that feeling in my body? See <u>sensation list</u>.

What situation or thoughts triggered this feeling?

What is this feeling telling me about what I need in this situation?

I am grateful for:

Daily Focus Planner

Write down three or more things or areas to focus on today that are meaningful.
Prioritize and take action!

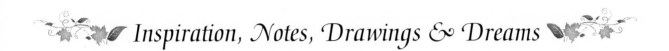 *Inspiration, Notes, Drawings & Dreams*

What happened today that helped me feel more connected to nature?

What had meaning for me today? What do I keep ignoring?

Date:_____

Watch the wind gently or wildly caress a tree today.

This Week's Affirmation (say it out loud)
I am filled with gratitude for my choices.

What is my Intention for the Day?

Consider using the intention list or a tarot or wisdom card. Your daily card might reflect a feeling, an intention, an opportunity, or a gift that you might not have thought of which gives you greater insight.

_____

_____

Question for the Day

How does this season gift me with what I need for my well-being? How can I get more out of these seasonal gifts?

_____

_____

Today I am feeling …

Name or identify my feelings. Refer back to <u>feeling list</u> if needed.

_____

_____

What is the sensation of that feeling in my body? See <u>sensation list</u>.

_____

What situation or thoughts triggered this feeling?

_____

_____

What is this feeling telling me about what I need in this situation?

_____

_____

I am grateful for:

_____   _____

_____   _____

Weekly Reflections and Inspiration

Use this space to explore your thoughts, readings or other experiences.
For example,

- What did I do this week that was meaningful?
- What were the thoughts, wisdom cards, or readings that captured my heart this week?
- How did nature reflect back to me something about myself?
- What ideas or inspirations do I want to explore further?

What are some empowering steps for next week?

Coloring Meditation

Or Color Outside the Lines!

Date:_____

If you can find water, what rainbows do you see?

This Week's Affirmation (say it out loud)
I am filled with gratitude for my choices.

What is my Intention for the Day?

Consider using the intention list or a tarot or wisdom card. Your daily card might reflect a feeling, an intention, an opportunity, or a gift that you might not have thought of which gives you greater insight.

Question for the Day

What outdoor activities relax, calm, and center me? How can I start including more of them in my daily life?

Today I am feeling ...
Name or identify my feelings. Refer back to <u>feeling list</u> if needed.

What is the sensation of that feeling in my body? See <u>sensation list</u>.

What situation or thoughts triggered this feeling?

What is this feeling telling me about what I need in this situation?

I am grateful for:

158

Daily Focus Planner

Write down three or more things or areas to focus on today that are meaningful.
Prioritize and take action!

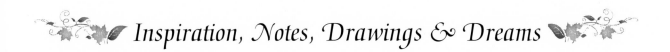 *Inspiration, Notes, Drawings & Dreams*

What happened today that helped me feel more connected to nature?

What had meaning for me today? What do I keep ignoring?

Date:_____

What is beginning to freeze or melt now?

This Week's Affirmation (say it out loud)
I am filled with gratitude for my choices.

What is my Intention for the Day?

Consider using the intention list or a tarot or wisdom card. Your daily card might reflect a feeling, an intention, an opportunity, or a gift that you might not have thought of which gives you greater insight.

Question for the Day

Do I trust my intuition and listen to that still small voice within? Give an example to illustrate this.

Today I am feeling …

Name or identify my feelings. Refer back to <u>feeling list</u> if needed.

What is the sensation of that feeling in my body? See <u>sensation list</u>.

What situation or thoughts triggered this feeling?

What is this feeling telling me about what I need in this situation?

I am grateful for:

Daily Focus Planner

Write down three or more things or areas to focus on today that are meaningful.
Prioritize and take action!

 *Inspiration, Notes, Drawings & Dreams*

What happened today that helped me feel more connected to nature?

What had meaning for me today? What do I keep ignoring?

*Date:*_____

What is the moon reflecting to you today?

This Week's Affirmation (say it out loud)
I am filled with gratitude for my choices.

What is my Intention for the Day?

Consider using the intention list or a tarot or wisdom card. Your daily card might reflect a feeling, an intention, an opportunity, or a gift that you might not have thought of which gives you greater insight.

_____

_____

Question for the Day

In this season, what is arising within me today that fills me up or wants to be released?

_____

_____

Today I am feeling …

Name or identify my feelings. Refer back to <u>feeling list</u> if needed.

_____

_____

What is the sensation of that feeling in my body? See <u>sensation list</u>.

_____

What situation or thoughts triggered this feeling?

_____

What is this feeling telling me about what I need in this situation?

_____

_____

I am grateful for:

_____ _____

_____ _____

Daily Focus Planner

Write down three or more things or areas to focus on today that are meaningful.
Prioritize and take action!

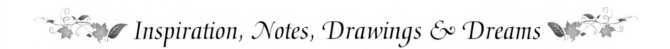 *Inspiration, Notes, Drawings & Dreams*

What happened today that helped me feel more connected to nature?

What had meaning for me today? What do I keep ignoring?

*Date:*_____

Find a spider web and notice its beauty.

This Week's Affirmation (say it out loud)
I am filled with gratitude for my choices.

What is my Intention for the Day?

Consider using the intention list or a tarot or wisdom card. Your daily card might reflect a feeling, an intention, an opportunity, or a gift that you might not have thought of which gives you greater insight.

_____

_____

Question for the Day

When I focus on the negative traits of another (or myself) how does that feel?

_____

_____

Today I am feeling …

Name or identify my feelings. Refer back to <u>feeling list</u> if needed.

_____

_____

What is the sensation of that feeling in my body? See <u>sensation list</u>.

_____

What situation or thoughts triggered this feeling?

_____

_____

What is this feeling telling me about what I need in this situation?

_____

_____

I am grateful for:

_____

_____

Daily Focus Planner

Write down three or more things or areas to focus on today that are meaningful.
Prioritize and take action!

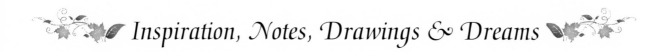 *Inspiration, Notes, Drawings & Dreams*

What happened today that helped me feel more connected to nature?

What had meaning for me today? What do I keep ignoring?

Date:_____

Explore outside for a natural treasure. What did you find?

This Week's Affirmation (say it out loud)
I am filled with gratitude for my choices.

What is my Intention for the Day?

Consider using the intention list or a tarot or wisdom card. Your daily card might reflect a feeling, an intention, an opportunity, or a gift that you might not have thought of which gives you greater insight.

_____

_____

_____

Question for the Day

When I focus on the positive traits of another (or myself) how does that feel?

_____

_____

_____

Today I am feeling ...

Name or identify my feelings. Refer back to feeling list if needed.

_____

_____

_____

What is the sensation of that feeling in my body? See sensation list.

_____

What situation or thoughts triggered this feeling?

_____

_____

What is this feeling telling me about what I need in this situation?

_____

_____

I am grateful for:

_____   _____

_____   _____

Daily Focus Planner

Write down three or more things or areas to focus on today that are meaningful.
Prioritize and take action!

 *Inspiration, Notes, Drawings & Dreams*

What happened today that helped me feel more connected to nature?

What had meaning for me today? What do I keep ignoring?

*Date:*_____

Send a plant some gratitude. Touch it and say hello.

This Week's Affirmation (say it out loud)
I am filled with gratitude for my choices.

What is my Intention for the Day?

Consider using the intention list or a tarot or wisdom card. Your daily card might reflect a feeling, an intention, an opportunity, or a gift that you might not have thought of which gives you greater insight.

Question for the Day

What kind of exercise or activity (indoors or outdoors) do I find most enjoyable?

Today I am feeling …

Name or identify my feelings. Refer back to feeling list if needed.

What is the sensation of that feeling in my body? See sensation list.

What situation or thoughts triggered this feeling?

What is this feeling telling me about what I need in this situation?

I am grateful for:

Monthly Reflections and Renewal

Review the five aspects of well-being. What aspect(s) of Physical, Relational, Mental, Spiritual and Financial and Career are showing up in my life this month?

_____
_____
_____
_____

How are my passions and actions moving me closer to living a fuller and more engaged life?

_____
_____
_____
_____

Am I happy with the results and feeling this brings to me?

_____
_____
_____
_____

What is or is not showing up for each aspect of well-being? Why might that be?

_____
_____
_____
_____

What would I change for next month so that I can gently course-correct and take actions that support me? Listen gently to what I am saying…

_____
_____
_____

Notes

You can find a calendar showing the phases of the moon and other notable astronomical events at **www.seasonalwidomjournal.com/calendar.**

Print the calendar, trim it to fit, and then paste it onto this page.

December

Sunday	Monday	Tuesday	Wednesday	Thursday	Friday	Saturday

Date:_____

Touch a rock, imagine how it got there.

This Week's Affirmation (say it out loud)
I am filled with gratitude for my choices.

What is my Intention for the Day?

Consider using the intention list or a tarot or wisdom card. Your daily card might reflect a feeling, an intention, an opportunity, or a gift that you might not have thought of which gives you greater insight.

_____
_____
_____

Question for the Day

In what aspects of my health am I feeling most fulfilled right now—physically, mentally, spiritually, emotionally?

_____
_____
_____

Today I am feeling …

Name or identify my feelings. Refer back to <u>feeling list</u> if needed.

_____
_____

What is the sensation of that feeling in my body? See <u>sensation list</u>.

_____

What situation or thoughts triggered this feeling?

_____
_____

What is this feeling telling me about what I need in this situation?

_____
_____

I am grateful for:

_____   _____
_____   _____

Weekly Reflections and Inspiration

Use this space to explore your thoughts, readings or other experiences.
For example,

- What did I do this week that was meaningful?
- What were the thoughts, wisdom cards, or readings that captured my heart this week?
- How did nature reflect back to me something about myself?
- What ideas or inspirations do I want to explore further?

What are some empowering steps for next week?

Coloring Meditation

Or Color Outside the Lines!

Date:_____

Trees are changing. What do you notice?

This Week's Affirmation (say it out loud)
I have loving kindness and compassion for myself.

What is my Intention for the Day?

Consider using the intention list or a tarot or wisdom card. Your daily card might reflect a feeling, an intention, an opportunity, or a gift that you might not have thought of which gives you greater insight.

_____

_____

_____

Question for the Day

How does Nature, Spirit, God, help support me emotionally?

_____

_____

_____

Today I am feeling ...

Name or identify my feelings. Refer back to <u>feeling list</u> if needed.

_____

_____

_____

What is the sensation of that feeling in my body? See <u>sensation list</u>.

_____

_____

What situation or thoughts triggered this feeling?

_____

_____

_____

What is this feeling telling me about what I need in this situation?

_____

_____

_____

I am grateful for:

_____   _____

_____   _____

Daily Focus Planner

Write down three or more things or areas to focus on today that are meaningful.
Prioritize and take action!

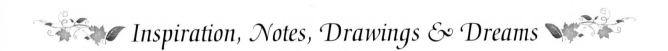 *Inspiration, Notes, Drawings & Dreams*

What happened today that helped me feel more connected to nature?

What had meaning for me today? What do I keep ignoring?

Date:_____

Find a sunbeam and give thanks to the sun.

This Week's Affirmation (say it out loud)
I have loving kindness and compassion for myself.

What is my Intention for the Day?

Consider using the intention list or a tarot or wisdom card. Your daily card might reflect a feeling, an intention, an opportunity, or a gift that you might not have thought of which gives you greater insight.

Question for the Day

What aspects of my well-being are being most nurtured and realized this season?

Today I am feeling …

Name or identify my feelings. Refer back to <u>feeling list</u> if needed.

What is the sensation of that feeling in my body? See <u>sensation list</u>.

What situation or thoughts triggered this feeling?

What is this feeling telling me about what I need in this situation?

I am grateful for:

Daily Focus Planner

Write down three or more things or areas to focus on today that are meaningful.
Prioritize and take action!

Inspiration, Notes, Drawings & Dreams

What happened today that helped me feel more connected to nature?

What had meaning for me today? What do I keep ignoring?

*Date:*_____

Put your finger in the ground. What did you notice?

This Week's Affirmation (say it out loud)
I have loving kindness and compassion for myself.

What is my Intention for the Day?

Consider using the intention list or a tarot or wisdom card. Your daily card might reflect a feeling, an intention, an opportunity, or a gift that you might not have thought of which gives you greater insight.

_____

_____

Question for the Day

When I think about money, how important is it to allow myself to rise to a higher level of financial prosperity? On a scale of 0-10, how committed am I to realizing a higher level of financial prosperity?

_____

_____

Today I am feeling …
Name or identify my feelings. Refer back to <u>feeling list</u> if needed.

_____

_____

What is the sensation of that feeling in my body? See <u>sensation list</u>.

_____

What situation or thoughts triggered this feeling?

_____

_____

What is this feeling telling me about what I need in this situation?

_____

_____

I am grateful for:

_____

_____

Daily Focus Planner

Write down three or more things or areas to focus on today that are meaningful.
Prioritize and take action!

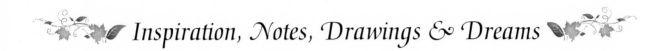 *Inspiration, Notes, Drawings & Dreams*

What happened today that helped me feel more connected to nature?

What had meaning for me today? What do I keep ignoring?

Date:_____

Pick up a stone today. Look for its uniqueness. Why did you pick it up?

This Week's Affirmation (say it out loud)
I have loving kindness and compassion for myself.

What is my Intention for the Day?

Consider using the intention list or a tarot or wisdom card. Your daily card might reflect a feeling, an intention, an opportunity, or a gift that you might not have thought of which gives you greater insight.

Question for the Day

What self-development book could I read to support an aspect of my health that needs greater attention? What expert could I consult?

Today I am feeling …
Name or identify my feelings. Refer back to <u>feeling list</u> if needed.

What is the sensation of that feeling in my body? See <u>sensation list</u>.

What situation or thoughts triggered this feeling?

What is this feeling telling me about what I need in this situation?

I am grateful for:

Daily Focus Planner

Write down three or more things or areas to focus on today that are meaningful.
Prioritize and take action!

 *Inspiration, Notes, Drawings & Dreams*

What happened today that helped me feel more connected to nature?

What had meaning for me today? What do I keep ignoring?

Date:_____

Go outside and see the rising sun.

This Week's Affirmation (say it out loud)
I have loving kindness and compassion for myself.

What is my Intention for the Day?

Consider using the intention list or a tarot or wisdom card. Your daily card might reflect a feeling, an intention, an opportunity, or a gift that you might not have thought of which gives you greater insight.

_____

_____

Question for the Day

• When I imagine myself at 90 years of age, having lived well, what do I see?

_____

_____

Today I am feeling …

Name or identify my feelings. Refer back to <u>feeling list</u> if needed.

_____

_____

What is the sensation of that feeling in my body? See <u>sensation list</u>.

_____

What situation or thoughts triggered this feeling?

_____

_____

What is this feeling telling me about what I need in this situation?

_____

_____

I am grateful for:

_____   _____

_____   _____

Daily Focus Planner

Write down three or more things or areas to focus on today that are meaningful.
Prioritize and take action!

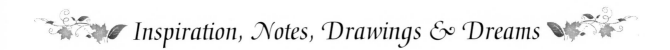 *Inspiration, Notes, Drawings & Dreams*

What happened today that helped me feel more connected to nature?

What had meaning for me today? What do I keep ignoring?

*Date:*_____

Listen for stillness.

This Week's Affirmation (say it out loud)
I have loving kindness and compassion for myself.

What is my Intention for the Day?

Consider using the intention list or a tarot or wisdom card. Your daily card might reflect a feeling, an intention, an opportunity, or a gift that you might not have thought of which gives you greater insight.

Question for the Day

• What am I doing to get in touch with and express my feelings to myself and others?

Today I am feeling …

Name or identify my feelings. Refer back to <u>feeling list</u> if needed.

What is the sensation of that feeling in my body? See <u>sensation list</u>.

What situation or thoughts triggered this feeling?

What is this feeling telling me about what I need in this situation?

I am grateful for:

Daily Focus Planner

Write down three or more things or areas to focus on today that are meaningful.
Prioritize and take action!

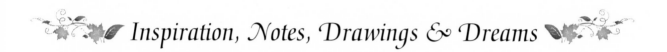 *Inspiration, Notes, Drawings & Dreams*

What happened today that helped me feel more connected to nature?

What had meaning for me today? What do I keep ignoring?

Date:_____

What plant wants to be seen today?

This Week's Affirmation (say it out loud)
I have loving kindness and compassion for myself.

What is my Intention for the Day?

Consider using the intention list or a tarot or wisdom card. Your daily card might reflect a feeling, an intention, an opportunity, or a gift that you might not have thought of which gives you greater insight.

_____

_____

Question for the Day

How am I supporting my physical body to feel strong, energetic, and alive?

_____

_____

Today I am feeling …

Name or identify my feelings. Refer back to <u>feeling list</u> if needed.

_____

_____

What is the sensation of that feeling in my body? See <u>sensation list</u>.

_____

What situation or thoughts triggered this feeling?

_____

What is this feeling telling me about what I need in this situation?

_____

_____

I am grateful for:

_____   _____

_____   _____

188

Weekly Reflections and Inspiration

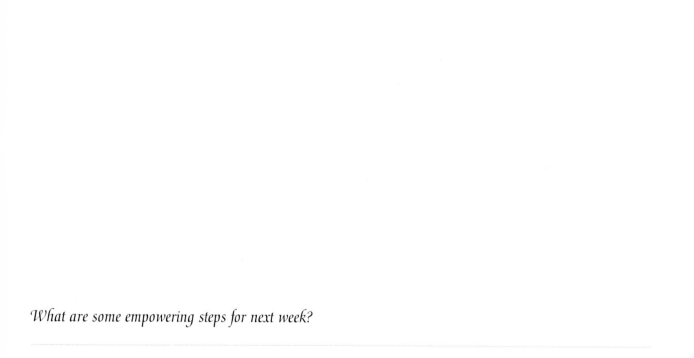

Use this space to explore your thoughts, readings or other experiences.
For example,

- What did I do this week that was meaningful?
- What were the thoughts, wisdom cards, or readings that captured my heart this week?
- How did nature reflect back to me something about myself?
- What ideas or inspirations do I want to explore further?

What are some empowering steps for next week?

Coloring Meditation

Or Color Outside the Lines!

*Date:*_____

Touch a plant today. What secrets will it share with you?

This Week's Affirmation (say it out loud)
Connected to all things, I am my own creator of love.

What is my Intention for the Day?

Consider using the intention list or a tarot or wisdom card. Your daily card might reflect a feeling, an intention, an opportunity, or a gift that you might not have thought of which gives you greater insight.

_____

_____

Question for the Day

What tools do I have and use to help me move when I want to from contracted feelings—like anxiety or sadness—to more expansive and relaxed feelings?

_____

_____

Today I am feeling …
Name or identify my feelings. Refer back to <u>feeling list</u> if needed.

_____

_____

What is the sensation of that feeling in my body? See <u>sensation list</u>.

_____

What situation or thoughts triggered this feeling?

_____

_____

What is this feeling telling me about what I need in this situation?

_____

_____

I am grateful for:

_____ _____

_____ _____

Daily Focus Planner

Write down three or more things or areas to focus on today that are meaningful.
Prioritize and take action!

 *Inspiration, Notes, Drawings & Dreams*

What happened today that helped me feel more connected to nature?

What had meaning for me today? What do I keep ignoring?

Date:_____

Take a walk at sunset.

This Week's Affirmation (say it out loud)
Connected to all things, I am my own creator of love.

What is my Intention for the Day?

Consider using the intention list or a tarot or wisdom card. Your daily card might reflect a feeling, an intention, an opportunity, or a gift that you might not have thought of which gives you greater insight.

_____

_____

Question for the Day

What creative endeavor could I engage in that could support an aspect of my health that needs greater attention?

_____

_____

Today I am feeling …
Name or identify my feelings. Refer back to <u>feeling list</u> if needed.

_____

_____

What is the sensation of that feeling in my body? See <u>sensation list</u>.

_____

What situation or thoughts triggered this feeling?

_____

_____

What is this feeling telling me about what I need in this situation?

_____

_____

I am grateful for:

_____

_____

Daily Focus Planner

Write down three or more things or areas to focus on today that are meaningful.
Prioritize and take action!

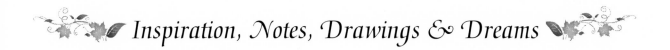 *Inspiration, Notes, Drawings & Dreams*

What happened today that helped me feel more connected to nature?

What had meaning for me today? What do I keep ignoring?

*Date:*_____

What is special to you about this season?

This Week's Affirmation (say it out loud)
Connected to all things, I am my own creator of love.

What is my Intention for the Day?

Consider using the intention list or a tarot or wisdom card. Your daily card might reflect a feeling, an intention, an opportunity, or a gift that you might not have thought of which gives you greater insight.

Question for the Day

What foods support my physical and emotional health these days? How is my eating part of a larger plan for my health and well-being?

Today I am feeling …
Name or identify my feelings. Refer back to <u>feeling list</u> if needed.

What is the sensation of that feeling in my body? See <u>sensation list</u>.

What situation or thoughts triggered this feeling?

What is this feeling telling me about what I need in this situation?

I am grateful for:

Daily Focus Planner

Write down three or more things or areas to focus on today that are meaningful.
Prioritize and take action!

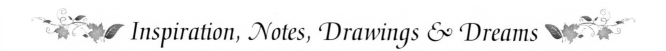 *Inspiration, Notes, Drawings & Dreams*

What happened today that helped me feel more connected to nature?

What had meaning for me today? What do I keep ignoring?

Date:_____

What animal or plant is calling to you today?

This Week's Affirmation (say it out loud)
Connected to all things, I am my own creator of love.

What is my Intention for the Day?

Consider using the intention list or a tarot or wisdom card. Your daily card might reflect a feeling, an intention, an opportunity, or a gift that you might not have thought of which gives you greater insight.

_____

_____

_____

Question for the Day

What feelings do I experience when I'm connected to something larger than myself?

_____

_____

_____

Today I am feeling …

Name or identify my feelings. Refer back to <u>feeling list</u> if needed.

_____

_____

_____

What is the sensation of that feeling in my body? See <u>sensation list</u>.

_____

What situation or thoughts triggered this feeling?

_____

_____

What is this feeling telling me about what I need in this situation?

_____

_____

_____

I am grateful for:

_____   _____

_____   _____

Daily Focus Planner

Write down three or more things or areas to focus on today that are meaningful.
Prioritize and take action!

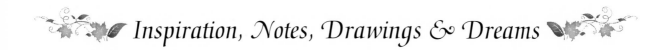 Inspiration, Notes, Drawings & Dreams

What happened today that helped me feel more connected to nature?

What had meaning for me today? What do I keep ignoring?

Date:_____

Hug a tree and say hello.

This Week's Affirmation (say it out loud)
Connected to all things, I am my own creator of love.

What is my Intention for the Day?

Consider using the intention list or a tarot or wisdom card. Your daily card might reflect a feeling, an intention, an opportunity, or a gift that you might not have thought of which gives you greater insight.

_____

_____

_____

Question for the Day
What or who reminds me of my essential goodness, who I really am?

_____

_____

_____

Today I am feeling …
Name or identify my feelings. Refer back to <u>feeling list</u> if needed.

_____

_____

_____

What is the sensation of that feeling in my body? See <u>sensation list</u>.

_____

What situation or thoughts triggered this feeling?

_____

_____

What is this feeling telling me about what I need in this situation?

_____

_____

_____

I am grateful for:

_____   _____

_____   _____

Daily Focus Planner

Write down three or more things or areas to focus on today that are meaningful.
Prioritize and take action!

 *Inspiration, Notes, Drawings & Dreams*

What happened today that helped me feel more connected to nature?

What had meaning for me today? What do I keep ignoring?

Date:_____

How are you honoring the land today?

This Week's Affirmation (say it out loud)
Connected to all things, I am my own creator of love.

What is my Intention for the Day?

Consider using the intention list or a tarot or wisdom card. Your daily card might reflect a feeling, an intention, an opportunity, or a gift that you might not have thought of which gives you greater insight.

_____

_____

_____

Question for the Day

What aspect of my health (physical, mental, emotional, or spiritual) do I want to focus on today? Why?

_____

_____

_____

Today I am feeling ...

Name or identify my feelings. Refer back to feeling list if needed.

_____

_____

_____

What is the sensation of that feeling in my body? See sensation list.

_____

What situation or thoughts triggered this feeling?

_____

_____

What is this feeling telling me about what I need in this situation?

_____

_____

I am grateful for:

_____ _____

_____ _____

Daily Focus Planner

Write down three or more things or areas to focus on today that are meaningful.
Prioritize and take action!

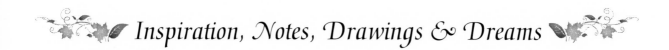 *Inspiration, Notes, Drawings & Dreams*

What happened today that helped me feel more connected to nature?

What had meaning for me today? What do I keep ignoring?

*Date:*_____

Look for shooting stars tonight.

This Week's Affirmation (say it out loud)
Connected to all things, I am my own creator of love.

What is my Intention for the Day?
Consider using the intention list or a tarot or wisdom card. Your daily card might reflect a feeling, an intention, an opportunity, or a gift that you might not have thought of which gives you greater insight.

_____

_____

_____

Question for the Day
How is my thinking supporting me today? How might it be sabotaging me? How can I shift my thinking if needed?

_____

_____

_____

Today I am feeling …
Name or identify my feelings. Refer back to <u>feeling list</u> if needed.

_____

_____

What is the sensation of that feeling in my body? See <u>sensation list</u>.

_____

What situation or thoughts triggered this feeling?

_____

_____

What is this feeling telling me about what I need in this situation?

_____

_____

I am grateful for:

_____   _____

_____   _____

Weekly Reflections and Inspiration

Use this space to explore your thoughts, readings or other experiences.
For example,

- What did I do this week that was meaningful?
- What were the thoughts, wisdom cards, or readings that captured my heart this week?
- How did nature reflect back to me something about myself?
- What ideas or inspirations do I want to explore further?

What are some empowering steps for next week?

Coloring Meditation

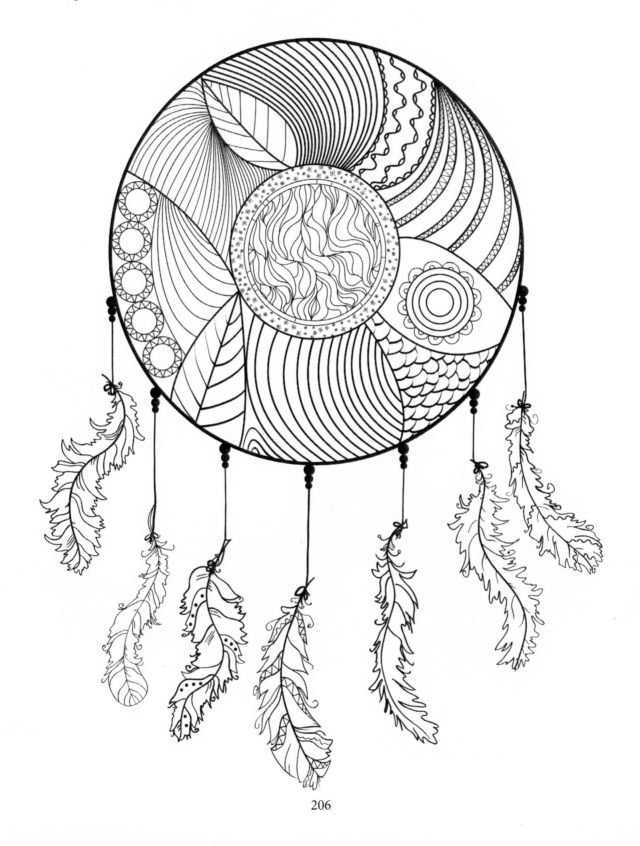

Or Color Outside the Lines!

*Date:*_____

What do you notice happening in your garden now?

This Week's Affirmation (say it out loud)
I am healing my body, mind, and spirit every day.

What is my Intention for the Day?
Consider using the intention list or a tarot or wisdom card. Your daily card might reflect a feeling, an intention, an opportunity, or a gift that you might not have thought of which gives you greater insight.

_____

_____

Question for the Day
Who in my life this past year really supported my wellness endeavors?

_____

_____

Today I am feeling …
Name or identify my feelings. Refer back to <u>feeling list</u> if needed.

_____

_____

What is the sensation of that feeling in my body? See <u>sensation list</u>.

_____

What situation or thoughts triggered this feeling?

_____

_____

What is this feeling telling me about what I need in this situation?

_____

_____

I am grateful for:

_____   _____

_____   _____

Daily Focus Planner

Write down three or more things or areas to focus on today that are meaningful.
Prioritize and take action!

 *Inspiration, Notes, Drawings & Dreams*

What happened today that helped me feel more connected to nature?

What had meaning for me today? What do I keep ignoring?

Date:_____

How can you give back to the land today?

This Week's Affirmation (say it out loud)
I am healing my body, mind, and spirit every day.

What is my Intention for the Day?

Consider using the intention list or a tarot or wisdom card. Your daily card might reflect a feeling, an intention, an opportunity, or a gift that you might not have thought of which gives you greater insight.

_____

_____

Question for the Day

What aspects of my well-being feel like a "should" and what areas feel like "I want to" for me? How can I convert shoulds to "get-to-dos?"

_____

_____

Today I am feeling ...
Name or identify my feelings. Refer back to <u>feeling list</u> if needed.

_____

_____

What is the sensation of that feeling in my body? See <u>sensation list</u>.

_____

What situation or thoughts triggered this feeling?

_____

_____

What is this feeling telling me about what I need in this situation?

_____

_____

I am grateful for:

_____

_____

Daily Focus Planner

Write down three or more things or areas to focus on today that are meaningful.
Prioritize and take action!

 *Inspiration, Notes, Drawings & Dreams*

What happened today that helped me feel more connected to nature?

What had meaning for me today? What do I keep ignoring?

Date:_____

What do you love about this evening?

This Week's Affirmation (say it out loud)
I am healing my body, mind, and spirit every day.

What is my Intention for the Day?
Consider using the intention list or a tarot or wisdom card. Your daily card might reflect a feeling, an intention, an opportunity, or a gift that you might not have thought of which gives you greater insight.

_____

_____

Question for the Day
How much time do I spend with positive people? With negative people? Would I change anything?

_____

_____

Today I am feeling …
Name or identify my feelings. Refer back to <u>feeling list</u> if needed.

_____

_____

What is the sensation of that feeling in my body? See <u>sensation list</u>.

_____

What situation or thoughts triggered this feeling?

_____

_____

What is this feeling telling me about what I need in this situation?

_____

_____

I am grateful for:

_____

_____

212

Daily Focus Planner

Write down three or more things or areas to focus on today that are meaningful.
Prioritize and take action!

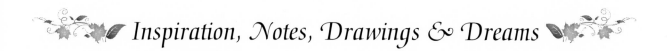 *Inspiration, Notes, Drawings & Dreams*

What happened today that helped me feel more connected to nature?

What had meaning for me today? What do I keep ignoring?

Date:_____

What adventure—big or small—will you take today?

This Week's Affirmation (say it out loud)
I am healing my body, mind, and spirit every day.

What is my Intention for the Day?

Consider using the intention list or a tarot or wisdom card. Your daily card might reflect a feeling, an intention, an opportunity, or a gift that you might not have thought of which gives you greater insight.

_____
_____
_____

Question for the Day

How often do I experience awe and wonder about the miracle of life?

_____
_____
_____

Today I am feeling …

Name or identify my feelings. Refer back to <u>feeling list</u> if needed.

_____
_____
_____

What is the sensation of that feeling in my body? See <u>sensation list</u>.

_____
_____

What situation or thoughts triggered this feeling?

_____
_____
_____

What is this feeling telling me about what I need in this situation?

_____
_____
_____

I am grateful for:

_____   _____
_____   _____

Daily Focus Planner

Write down three or more things or areas to focus on today that are meaningful.
Prioritize and take action!

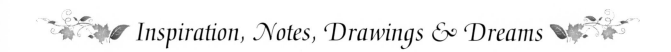 *Inspiration, Notes, Drawings & Dreams*

What happened today that helped me feel more connected to nature?

What had meaning for me today? What do I keep ignoring?

Date:_____

Invite someone to observe a tree with you. Share what you see together.

This Week's Affirmation (say it out loud)
I am healing my body, mind, and spirit every day.

What is my Intention for the Day?

Consider using the intention list or a tarot or wisdom card. Your daily card might reflect a feeling, an intention, an opportunity, or a gift that you might not have thought of which gives you greater insight.

_____
_____
_____

Question for the Day

Who really supported my wellness endeavors in this past year?

_____
_____
_____

Today I am feeling …

Name or identify my feelings. Refer back to feeling list if needed.

_____
_____
_____

What is the sensation of that feeling in my body? See sensation list.

_____

What situation or thoughts triggered this feeling?

_____
_____

What is this feeling telling me about what I need in this situation?

_____
_____

I am grateful for:

_____   _____
_____   _____

Daily Focus Planner

Write down three or more things or areas to focus on today that are meaningful.
Prioritize and take action!

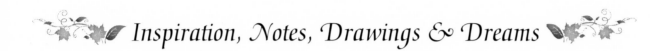 *Inspiration, Notes, Drawings & Dreams*

What happened today that helped me feel more connected to nature?

What had meaning for me today? What do I keep ignoring?

*Date:*_____

Check the sky for rainbows.

This Week's Affirmation (say it out loud)
I am healing my body, mind, and spirit every day.

What is my Intention for the Day?

Consider using the intention list or a tarot or wisdom card. Your daily card might reflect a feeling, an intention, an opportunity, or a gift that you might not have thought of which gives you greater insight.

_____

_____

Question for the Day

What habits or practices have I created for myself that support my health and well-being? Am I using them regularly? What would support me to use them more?

_____

_____

Today I am feeling …
Name or identify my feelings. Refer back to <u>feeling list</u> if needed.

_____

_____

What is the sensation of that feeling in my body? See <u>sensation list</u>.

_____

What situation or thoughts triggered this feeling?

_____

_____

What is this feeling telling me about what I need in this situation?

_____

_____

I am grateful for:

_____   _____

_____   _____

Daily Focus Planner

Write down three or more things or areas to focus on today that are meaningful.
Prioritize and take action!

 *Inspiration, Notes, Drawings & Dreams*

What happened today that helped me feel more connected to nature?

What had meaning for me today? What do I keep ignoring?

*Date:*_____

What will you do to get ready for this change in season?

This Week's Affirmation (say it out loud)
I am healing my body, mind, and spirit every day.

What is my Intention for the Day?

Consider using the intention list or a tarot or wisdom card. Your daily card might reflect a feeling, an intention, an opportunity, or a gift that you might not have thought of which gives you greater insight.

_____

_____

Question for the Day
I feel strong when I…

_____

_____

Today I am feeling …
Name or identify my feelings. Refer back to <u>feeling list</u> if needed.

_____

_____

What is the sensation of that feeling in my body? See <u>sensation list</u>.

_____

What situation or thoughts triggered this feeling?

_____

What is this feeling telling me about what I need in this situation?

_____

_____

I am grateful for:

_____   _____

_____   _____

Weekly Reflections and Inspiration

Use this space to explore your thoughts, readings or other experiences.
For example,

- What did I do this week that was meaningful?
- What were the thoughts, wisdom cards, or readings that captured my heart this week?
- How did nature reflect back to me something about myself?
- What ideas or inspirations do I want to explore further?

What are some empowering steps for next week?

Coloring Meditation

Or Color Outside the Lines!

Date:_____

What do you notice about the season changing?

This Week's Affirmation (say it out loud)
I am free to be present in this moment. I listen to, honor, and stay with myself whatever I'm feeling.

What is my Intention for the Day?

Consider using the intention list or a tarot or wisdom card. Your daily card might reflect a feeling, an intention, an opportunity, or a gift that you might not have thought of which gives you greater insight.

_____

_____

Question for the Day

When I think about the year ahead, how do I want to feel most of the time?

_____

_____

Today I am feeling …

Name or identify my feelings. Refer back to <u>feeling list</u> if needed.

_____

_____

What is the sensation of that feeling in my body? See <u>sensation list</u>.

_____

What situation or thoughts triggered this feeling?

_____

_____

What is this feeling telling me about what I need in this situation?

_____

_____

I am grateful for:

_____   _____

_____   _____

224

Daily Focus Planner

Write down three or more things or areas to focus on today that are meaningful.
Prioritize and take action!

 *Inspiration, Notes, Drawings & Dreams*

What happened today that helped me feel more connected to nature?

What had meaning for me today? What do I keep ignoring?

*Date:*_____

Feel the air on your face this morning or evening. What do you notice?

This Week's Affirmation (say it out loud)
I am free to be present in this moment. I listen to, honor, and stay with myself whatever I'm feeling.

What is my Intention for the Day?
Consider using the intention list or a tarot or wisdom card. Your daily card might reflect a feeling, an intention, an opportunity, or a gift that you might not have thought of which gives you greater insight.

_____

_____

Question for the Day
What did I do recently that took some courage? (Courage literally means coming from the heart.)

_____

_____

Today I am feeling …
Name or identify my feelings. Refer back to <u>feeling list</u> if needed.

_____

_____

What is the sensation of that feeling in my body? See <u>sensation list</u>.

_____

What situation or thoughts triggered this feeling?

_____

_____

What is this feeling telling me about what I need in this situation?

_____

_____

I am grateful for:

_____   _____

_____   _____

Daily Focus Planner

Write down three or more things or areas to focus on today that are meaningful.
Prioritize and take action!

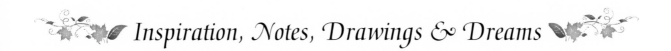 *Inspiration, Notes, Drawings & Dreams*

What happened today that helped me feel more connected to nature?

What had meaning for me today? What do I keep ignoring?

Date:_____

How does the sun feel on your skin today?

This Week's Affirmation (say it out loud)
I am free to be present in this moment. I listen to, honor, and stay with myself whatever I'm feeling.

What is my Intention for the Day?

Consider using the intention list or a tarot or wisdom card. Your daily card might reflect a feeling, an intention, an opportunity, or a gift that you might not have thought of which gives you greater insight.

_____

_____

Question for the Day

In what areas of my life do I feel most confident? What did I do to get that way? How can I apply that to other areas of my life where I feel less confident?

_____

_____

Today I am feeling …
Name or identify my feelings. Refer back to feeling list if needed.

_____

_____

What is the sensation of that feeling in my body? See sensation list.

_____

What situation or thoughts triggered this feeling?

_____

_____

What is this feeling telling me about what I need in this situation?

_____

_____

I am grateful for:

_____ _____

_____ _____

Daily Focus Planner

Write down three or more things or areas to focus on today that are meaningful.
Prioritize and take action!

 *Inspiration, Notes, Drawings & Dreams*

What happened today that helped me feel more connected to nature?

What had meaning for me today? What do I keep ignoring?

*Date:*_____

What are plants doing now to prepare for the coming season?

This Week's Affirmation (say it out loud)
I am free to be present in this moment. I listen to, honor, and stay with myself whatever I'm feeling.

What is my Intention for the Day?

Consider using the intention list or a tarot or wisdom card. Your daily card might reflect a feeling, an intention, an opportunity, or a gift that you might not have thought of which gives you greater insight.

_____

_____

Question for the Day

What courses, teachers, mentors, coaches, and trainers would I enjoy learning from to support my inner health and well-being? What steps am I taking now and what are my next steps in engaging with them?

_____

_____

Today I am feeling …
Name or identify my feelings. Refer back to <u>feeling list</u> if needed.

_____

_____

What is the sensation of that feeling in my body? See <u>sensation list</u>.

_____

What situation or thoughts triggered this feeling?

_____

_____

What is this feeling telling me about what I need in this situation?

_____

_____

I am grateful for:

_____   _____

_____   _____

Daily Focus Planner

Write down three or more things or areas to focus on today that are meaningful.
Prioritize and take action!

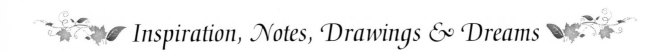 Inspiration, Notes, Drawings & Dreams

What happened today that helped me feel more connected to nature?

What had meaning for me today? What do I keep ignoring?

Date:_____

What animals are you noticing or not noticing these days?

This Week's Affirmation (say it out loud)
I am free to be present in this moment. I listen to, honor, and stay with myself whatever I'm feeling.

What is my Intention for the Day?
Consider using the intention list or a tarot or wisdom card. Your daily card might reflect a feeling, an intention, an opportunity, or a gift that you might not have thought of which gives you greater insight.

_____
_____

Question for the Day
Where am I, who am I with, and what am I doing when I am my most inspired?

_____
_____

Today I am feeling …
Name or identify my feelings. Refer back to <u>feeling list</u> if needed.

_____
_____

What is the sensation of that feeling in my body? See <u>sensation list</u>.

_____

What situation or thoughts triggered this feeling?

_____

What is this feeling telling me about what I need in this situation?

_____
_____

I am grateful for:

_____   _____
_____   _____

Daily Focus Planner

Write down three or more things or areas to focus on today that are meaningful.
Prioritize and take action!

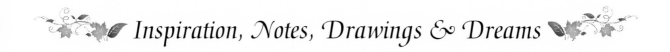 *Inspiration, Notes, Drawings & Dreams*

What happened today that helped me feel more connected to nature?

What had meaning for me today? What do I keep ignoring?

Date:_____

Watch for a special cloud in the sky and give it thanks.

This Week's Affirmation (say it out loud)
I am free to be present in this moment. I listen to, honor, and stay with myself whatever I'm feeling.

What is my Intention for the Day?

Consider using the intention list or a tarot or wisdom card. Your daily card might reflect a feeling, an intention, an opportunity, or a gift that you might not have thought of which gives you greater insight.

_____

_____

_____

Question for the Day

What am I giving up on right now? What are my reasons? Are they excuses or do I really need to move on?

_____

_____

_____

Today I am feeling ...

Name or identify my feelings. Refer back to <u>feeling list</u> if needed.

_____

_____

What is the sensation of that feeling in my body? See <u>sensation list</u>.

_____

What situation or thoughts triggered this feeling?

_____

_____

What is this feeling telling me about what I need in this situation?

_____

_____

I am grateful for:

_____   _____

_____   _____

Daily Focus Planner

Write down three or more things or areas to focus on today that are meaningful.
Prioritize and take action!

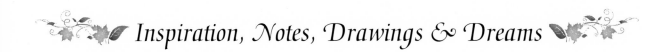

Inspiration, Notes, Drawings & Dreams

What happened today that helped me feel more connected to nature?

What had meaning for me today? What do I keep ignoring?

Date:_____

What is the light doing early in the mornings now?

This Week's Affirmation (say it out loud)
I am free to be present in this moment. I listen to, honor, and stay with myself whatever I'm feeling.

What is my Intention for the Day?
Consider using the intention list or a tarot or wisdom card. Your daily card might reflect a feeling, an intention, an opportunity, or a gift that you might not have thought of which gives you greater insight.

_____
_____
_____

Question for the Day
When do I feel least strong and powerful? What do I most need at those times or in those situations?

_____
_____
_____

Today I am feeling …
Name or identify my feelings. Refer back to feeling list if needed.

_____
_____
_____

What is the sensation of that feeling in my body? See sensation list.

_____

What situation or thoughts triggered this feeling?

_____
_____

What is this feeling telling me about what I need in this situation?

_____
_____

I am grateful for:

_____ _____
_____ _____

Weekly Reflections and Inspiration

Use this space to explore your thoughts, readings or other experiences.
For example,

- What did I do this week that was meaningful?
- What were the thoughts, wisdom cards, or readings that captured my heart this week?
- How did nature reflect back to me something about myself?
- What ideas or inspirations do I want to explore further?

What are some empowering steps for next week?

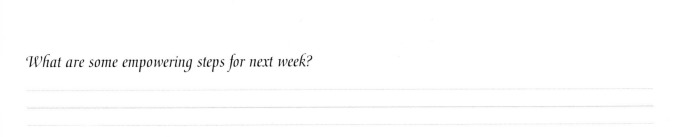

Coloring Meditation

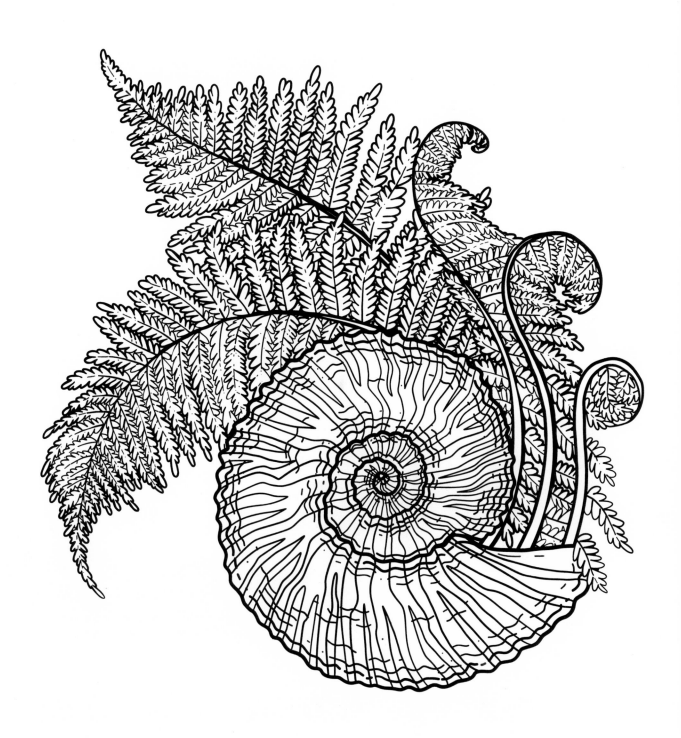

Or Color Outside the Lines!

Date:_____

Take a brisk walk today and see what you notice.

This Week's Affirmation (say it out loud)
My body knows how to heal itself. I cherish my life path.

What is my Intention for the Day?
Consider using the intention list or a tarot or wisdom card. Your daily card might reflect a feeling, an intention, an opportunity, or a gift that you might not have thought of which gives you greater insight.

_____
_____
_____

Question for the Day
Am I fully allowing myself to learn and grow? Give some examples of how I am doing that for myself.

_____
_____
_____

Today I am feeling …
Name or identify my feelings. Refer back to <u>feeling list</u> if needed.

_____
_____
_____

What is the sensation of that feeling in my body? See <u>sensation list</u>.

_____

What situation or thoughts triggered this feeling?

_____
_____

What is this feeling telling me about what I need in this situation?

_____
_____

I am grateful for:

_____   _____
_____   _____

Daily Focus Planner

Write down three or more things or areas to focus on today that are meaningful.
Prioritize and take action!

 *Inspiration, Notes, Drawings & Dreams*

What happened today that helped me feel more connected to nature?

What had meaning for me today? What do I keep ignoring?

Date:_____

Go outside and enjoy the last day of the year.

This Week's Affirmation (say it out loud)
My body knows how to heal itself. I cherish my life path.

What is my Intention for the Day?
Consider using the intention list or a tarot or wisdom card. Your daily card might reflect a feeling, an intention, an opportunity, or a gift that you might not have thought of which gives you greater insight.

_____

_____

Question for the Day
When I reflect on the past year, what were my big wellness wins? 0

_____

_____

_____

Today I am feeling …
Name or identify my feelings. Refer back to feeling list if needed.

_____

_____

What is the sensation of that feeling in my body? See sensation list.

_____

What situation or thoughts triggered this feeling?

_____

_____

What is this feeling telling me about what I need in this situation?

_____

_____

I am grateful for:

_____   _____

_____   _____

Monthly Reflections and Renewal

Review the five aspects of well-being. What aspect(s) of Physical, Relational, Mental, Spiritual and Financial and Career are showing up in my life this month?

How are my passions and actions moving me closer to living a fuller and more engaged life?

Am I happy with the results and feeling this brings to me?

What is or is not showing up for each aspect of well-being? Why might that be?

What would I change for next month so that I can gently course-correct and take actions that support me? Listen gently to what I am saying…

Notes

About the Author

Karin Lubin, Ed.D., is a coach, trainer and leadership consultant driven by a desire to inspire and energize people and teams through the power of love.

After a career as a public school teacher, administrator and leadership consultant in diverse communities, she became the Global Director of the Passion Test Programs assisting individuals, businesses and young people seeking meaningful and fulfilling lives. Karin's lifelong passion for deep self-discovery and connecting others to their brilliance guides all of her work and creative endeavors.

She and her husband, live in Santa Fe, New Mexico.
Visit karinlubin.com

Go Deeper to Be Greater!

1. **Go deeper within yourself**. Find all four Seasonal Wisdom Journals at **karinlubin.com/author.**

2. **Engage in illuminating conversations.** Connect to a community of like-minded souls through journaling, seasonal reflections, dialogue, and practical and spiritual virtual discussions. Learn more about your seasonal online Wisdom Journaling Circle at **karinlubin.com/wisdom-circle.**

3. **Experience emotional resilience** and greater balance in your life. Become more heart-centered and real. Explore your intuitive nature that is ready to be set free. Ignite your passion and your authenticity— for yourself and your business—through Karin's one-on-one coaching. Learn more at **karinlubin.com/ coaching.**

4. **Connect with other deep thinkers.** Join our free community on Facebook, *Busy People and Deep Thinkers,* **karinlubin.com/facebook,** for resources to help you to go deeper to become greater. You can also post on your favorite social platform using **#MyLifeThroughTheSeasons.**

5. **Become an author** and help your clients deepen their practice using your own body of work adapted to journaling. Co-create your own wisdom journal using our turn-key Professional Package. Learn more at **karinlubin.com/professional.**

Made in United States
North Haven, CT
06 September 2023

41208023R00150